TOWARD
A
NEW BRAIN

This intriguing series encompasses exciting trends and discoveries in areas of human exploration and progress: astronomy, anthropology, biology, physics, geology, medicine, health, genetics, and evolution. Sometimes controversial, these timely volumes present stimulating new points of view about our universe . . . and ourselves.

TOWARD
A
NEW BRAIN

Evolution
and the Human Mind

STUART LITVAK
and
A. WAYNE SENZEE

PRENTICE-HALL, INC.
Englewood Cliffs, New Jersey 07632

Library of Congress Cataloging-in-Publication Data

Litvak, Stuart.
Toward a new brain.

(Frontiers of science)
"A Spectrum book"—T.p. verso.
Bibliography: p.
Includes index.
1. Brain—Evolution. 2. Human evolution.
I. Senzee, A. Wayne. II. Title. III. Series.
QP376.L58 1986   152   85-31709
ISBN 0-13-926049-8

10 9 8 7 6 5 4 3 2 1

CONTENTS

PREFACE

*What we need . . . is a new "paradigm"—a new vision
of reality; a fundamental change in our thoughts, perceptions, and values. The beginnings of this change, of
the shift from the mechanistic to the holistic conception of reality, are already visible in all fields and
are likely to dominate the present decade.*

—FRITJOF CAPRA
The Turning Point (1982)

Cambridge scientist and thinker Edward de Bono has suggested an
analogy between scientific thinking and the digging of holes. The hole
is the area of concern (e.g., a certain theory about something), and the
digging is the study and research. De Bono points out that all too often
scientists tend to become transfixed on some particular hole, digging it
deeper and bigger, in the hope that it will become an altogether better
(or "established") hole. But de Bono notes that ". . . if the hole is in the
wrong place, then no amount of improvement is going to put it in the
right place." And, "No matter how obvious this may seem to every
digger, it is still easier to go on digging in the same hole than to start all
over again in a new place."[1]

In looking at evolution, de Bono's analogy is apt. The Darwinian
theory may be viewed as an exhausted, 120-year-old archeological dig
that has held the majority of us in conceptual captivity, having grown
to such a size that it can easily hold in its depths practically every
scientist alive today, almost all their students, and the bulk of the
public as well.

As we will try to show in this book, however, the Darwinian hole
must now be abandoned. The time to dig elsewhere is long overdue.
Although evolution itself cannot be denied (much to the chagrin of
"creationists" who, like the mole, suffer from impaired vision, a consequence of unmitigated burrowing in their own labyrinthine hole),
Darwinian theory will be revealed in these pages to be a largely inadequate explanation of evolution.

By digging elsewhere we will begin to see that another view of
evolution—one that actually preceded Darwinism by centuries, known
loosely as "transformism"—provides us with a much more realistic
account.

One of the major difficulties of biological science has been its effort at excluding all nonscientific thought about evolution as qualitatively irrelevant to the subject. Biologists consider the field to be their eminent domain. Unfortunately, they have not yet struck pay dirt in their experimental diggings and, with a few exceptions, are only making it more difficult to dig elsewhere, to stay with our metaphor. Western science definitively restricts itself to the study of physical, material phenomena; there has traditionally been no room for concern with immaterial properties (mind, consciousness, meaning, and all things "psychic"). Scientists have subscribed only to the mechanics and explanation of rational reductionism. As a group, they view the universe and life as a mere conglomeration of physiochemical processes and interactions.

As philosopher Henryk Skolimowski describes this devaluation in his book *Eco-Philosophy*, life can be reduced in scientific terms to chemical processes, then to base physics, but not without degrading the idea of life itself. All this may tell us something about the raw materials and brute forces upon which life is built, yet these are not life. To think, as many scientists do, that such physiochemical constituents are the essence of life is akin to thinking that 14-carat gold is the random combination of a few metals. "We cannot escape the feeling," concludes Skolimowski, "that this is cheapening the meaning of life."[2]

In actuality, evolution is an infinite landscape with vaguely definable horizons. Within that panorama the sciences have developed as a more or less (too often less) objective attempt to make solid sense of the physical surroundings. That is to say that they are limited by the very conditions of what they study, and hence they are contained by it, not vice versa. Albeit, evolution is what is happening at the outer *and* inner horizons, including the material as well as the "immaterial," as we so handily call it. As a broad and central phenomenon, it is the prime integrator that encompasses all aspects of mental, physical, and spiritual life. Evolution offers mysteries that science as it stands is functionally unequipped to deal with, often even to define.

The most open-minded scientists admit to the failure of their various disciplines to synthesize their knowledge to a more fully human understanding of reality. The leading physicist Erwin Schroedinger, for instance, compares the scientific picture of reality with an impressive blueprint of figures and facts that is still vastly incomplete. It tells us a great deal about the order of phenomena in nature but says nothing about the relative mean or relevant meaning of that order, that which ultimately matters to us. It ". . . knows nothing of beautiful and ugly, good or bad, God and eternity."[3]

Yet these are the things that consciousness seeks out as higher truth. And consciousness is the crown of evolution.

The purpose of this book is to discuss evolution within a comprehensive perspective, to reveal the *idée fixe* effect of Darwinism while exposing clearly its net inadequacy as a viable explanation. Alternative, reasonable viewpoints will be presented. You are not invited to believe them, only to consider them.

Although our intention is to make the subject as accessible as possible to the reader who is not a scientist, certain technicalities cannot be avoided because of the inclusion of the cited research and theory. The finer details are sometimes there to satisfy scientists who are steeped exclusively in Darwinian theory and to reach them in their own idiom.

The importance of providing an alternative world view to that of Darwinism has not been stressed enough, probably because it is not widely recognized how deeply an implied Darwinian philosophy has permeated our culture, values, thinking, and behavior. As Skolimowski and others have pointed out, a social Darwinism has laid strong roots in our sociopolitical ground, in which competition, "free" enterprise, and entrepreneurial aggression are twisted into an equation for survival of the fittest. The devil take the hindmost.

Against this background, evolution (as a dynamic rather than a theory) can be seen and revalued in a broader, brighter light. Social equity, collective self-fulfillment, and an abridgement of the gap between materialism and spirituality can replace the destructive logic of much of our formal thought as it influences the world today.

Evolution is the transcending reality of life. In the mystic's parlance it is the "unfolding of the moment." It is change in its most profound sense—at once process and progress. We are in a season in human history that is most favorable and crucial for the planting of new evolutionary seeds of thought. With proper care and attention, the resulting yield can provide ample abundance and an improved outlook for all of us, as well as for those to come.

ACKNOWLEDGMENTS

Many thanks to Nora Burba and Candace Smith for their editorial expertise, and to Jane Manley and Kathy Jones for typing the manuscript and its many revisions. Appreciation is extended to our editor, Mary Kennan, who has, as always, provided her valuable trust and support. Thanks. too, to our good friends, including Everet Hetzel, Jeff Heimer, Mac MacFarland, Rich Holmes, and Dr. Joe Battersby.

The most beautiful experience we can have is the mysterious. It is the fundamental emotion which stands at the cradle of true art and science. Whoever does not notice it and can no longer wonder, no longer marvel, is as good as dead, and his eyes are dimmed. . . . A knowledge of the existence of something we cannot penetrate, our perceptions of the profoundest reason and the most radiant beauty, which only in their most primitive forms are accessible to our minds—it is this knowledge and this emotion that constitute true religiosity; in this sense, and in this alone, I am a deeply religious man.

—ALBERT EINSTEIN

INTRODUCTION

The past 120 years have seen many scores of good books on evolution, beginning with Darwin's *The Origin of Species* in 1859. Of these thousands, a few have become classics, such as Huxley's *Evolution: The Modern Synthesis* (1942), Simpson's *The Major Features of Evolution* (1953), Eisley's *The Immense Journey* (1958), and Dobzhansky's *Mankind Evolving* (1962). In just the past decade, due in part to a revival of the creation/evolution debate, a spate of new tomes on the subject have appeared. A number of these are excellent treatments, and several have become bestsellers (e.g., Sagan's *The Dragons of Eden*, Bateson's *Mind and Nature*, and Gould's *The Panda's Thumb*).

Although both the creationists and neo-Darwinists now seem to be running out of wind in huffing and puffing at the straw in each others' arguments, genuine interest in evolution continues to grow. This interest ranges well beyond the strictly scientific and religious forums, showing up most markedly in the areas of personal development, higher consciousness, and spirituality. Professional and layman, specialist and generalist alike are seeking a more holistic comprehension of the phenomenon. To help fill that need is the express purpose of *Toward a New Brain*.

Despite the abundance of impressive technical and hypothetical expositions on evolution, very few actually break much ground beyond classical Darwinism, nor do they present the subject as a vital and ongoing process. The shortcoming is one that is inherent in the reductionism of Darwinism itself. Because evolution is equated with Darwinism in most people's minds, the first task of this book is to distinguish between evolution as a reasonably established fact (including empirical evidence) and theories or explanations of evolution. *Toward a New Brain* clearly defines this distinction. Consequently, Darwinism is revealed as a conceptually inadequate explanation of the greater fact, with a parallel lack of personal meaning for the individual. *Toward a New Brain* is in concert with the new world view taking shape both in science and outside of it. Although its alternative interpretation of morphological change has its obscure origins rooted in the past, much of the cited research supporting it is new, and you may herein share the novelty and authentic excitement in rediscovering a buried treasure of evolutionary theory.

Traditionally referred to as "transformism," the main ideas and postulates of this position fit the living facts of natural evolution much better than historical Darwinism or its several modern-day variations. During the past few decades a steady current of research data has been strengthening the transformist theory. The data comes from biology, biochemistry, neurology, medicine, psychology, anthropology, ethology, and related disciplines. Through these, evolutionary thinking is being gradually expanded, deepened, and refined.

Past holders of the transformist view included Lamarck, Goethe, Bergson, Spencer, Samuel Butler, Nietzsche, and Bernard Shaw, among others. Arthur Koestler, Theodore Roszak, and Lyall Watson are only several of its prominent contemporary exponents. The present book traces the seminal insights of all these and aligns them with the work of the latest pioneers, such as Rupert Sheldrake. Special care is taken to clarify the complexities while avoiding oversimplification. It is hoped that transformist theory is thereby advanced for the reader, in both sophistication and value.

It is at last being recognized, even by some Darwinists, that psychological dynamics are indissolubly combined with biological ones in evolutionary processes. Although these connections are generally ignored in most other books, they have a paramount place in the following pages. Psychology, in fact, is given a major role in the vast theatre of evolution, with biology playing a secondary or epiphenomenal part. Except for the seminal writings of Lamarck, Butler, and Bergson, almost every article and book published on the topic in the past 125 years has not only failed to see mind, consciousness, and experience as central in the evolutionary drama, but in most cases has excluded them completely. So the framework of evolution has to date remained a woefully incomplete one, lacking even a finished conceptual foundation.

Yet, as you will find, psychodynamic factors have always accompanied anatomical or structural developments, and indeed they probably even precede and in some way alter them, being the precursors, in effect, of physical change.

The implications of a new evolutionary world view for human progress in all realms of life are illuminated in *Toward a New Brain*. Those persons with religious and spiritual concerns will find ample material for meditation, and the chapter on the brain and learning should be a bonus, especially for educators. For the scientifically minded, the ideas presented herein run against the grain of prevailing thought and, hence, will meet resistance or support, depending upon one's particular bent. If at minimum this book stimulates your mind and generates some productive thought and discussion, then it will have served its essential purpose.

Chapter One

EVOLUTION
OR CREATION?

When we examine a process like evolution, which brought about such prodigies as human intelligence and conscience, we should, therefore, never take the rapidity or slowness of the event into consideration. What is "rapid" to us in relation to the rhythm of our life, of our sensorial and intellectual mechanisms, conditioned by the structure of our brains will be "slow" for an ephemeral insect with a life span of only a few days. To an imaginary being, with a life span of ten thousand million years, evolution would seem very rapid. To God, whom we cannot even conceive in relation to time, it may well have been "instantaneous."

Lecomte du Noüy,
Human Destiny

Evolution. You would think that in this day and age the word would hardly stir more than a few indignant grunts and whispers, that not many people would bother again to join heated debates about whether the human species sprang forth from the loins of Adam or the groin of a monkey. But despite all the scientific research to substantiate the phenomenon of evolution that has accumulated since the Scopes trial of 1925 to this day, Darwin is back on trial in what is being referred to as "Scopes II." Again, evolution is under attack by creationists who want equal time for their biblical theories in biology classes and textbooks.

Very simply, and according to the typical dictionary definition, *evolution* refers to "an orderly and progressive development" governed by certain unknown—but exact—laws. For a more scientific definition, the following is from a modern textbook:

> Organic evolution is a series of partial or complete and irreversible transformations of the genetic composition of populations, based principally upon altered interactions with their environments. It consists chiefly of adaptive radiations into new environments, adjustments to environmental changes that take place in a particular habitat, and the origin of new ways for exploiting existing habitats. These adaptive changes occasionally give rise to greater complexity of developmental pattern, of physiological reactions, and of interactions between populations and their environments.[1]

Most theorists, scientists, and writers on the subject of evolution agree that the key distinguishing feature is *transformation*, and that the transformation or metamorphosis must be progressive (as opposed to regressive or stagnant).

Since Darwin, the notion of evolution has primarily been referred to the three usual classes of terrestrial life: plants, animals, humans. Of late, however, evolution has been seen as operating at other levels as well—especially the cosmological. Whether the cosmos is therefore "alive" or a "life form" is yet to be resolved.

A basic premise of this book is that evolution is universal and that when it is related to the accepted categories of living things (i.e., plant, animal, human), the evidence for evolution is overwhelming. The evidence for the evolution of life includes the following: paleontology (bones and fossils), comparative anatomy, morphology, embryology, and comparative biochemistry. The techniques for establishing the evidence are sophisticated, including carbon-14 dating procedures, chromosomal microanalysis, and serological analysis.

Although devout creationists still rail against what they misinterpret as a threat to their faith, they cannot deny the evidence. In actuality, the issue may no longer legitimately be viewed as that of creationism versus evolution but of how the creationists are to reconcile evolution within their own religious framework. If you accept a fixed, *literal* interpretation of the Bible, for example, then it is doubtful whether you will arrive at the reconciliation. In that case, you will have to keep the Bible and evolution separate. But this sort of thinking is not likely to succeed.

The beginning of life on earth dates back three billion years, with modern man having evolved more than 50,000 years ago. These facts do not cause problems for certain religions, such as those of Eastern origin, but they can produce difficulties for those religions founded upon the literal interpretation of the Bible. However, if the Bible were to be interpreted allegorically, the problems would diminish. In this interpretation, Biblical verses about creation, Adam and Eve, and so on could be considered as symbolic—that is, as representing *turning points* in the evolutionary course of life. Or terms such as heaven, hell, angels, devil, and the like could be seen as symbolic of *mental states.* By interpreting the Bible in this sense, one can minimize the difficulties in accepting evolution.

In his brilliant book *The Seven Mysteries of Life,* Guy Murchie reveals clearly how a symbolic interpretation of the Book of Genesis can easily resolve the fruitless creationist–evolutionist conflict. Murchie explains how the publication of Darwin's *Origin of Species* was a bombshell only because it was taken (if not believed) as literally as the Bible was by a society theologized in literalism. For those, however, who chose to understand the Scriptures symbolically, evolution could provide a logical accounting of "How the Creator may have carried out his creation."[2]

The gist of the literalist problem is that it conceives the passage of time as absolute or clocklike, with the act of world creation measured as six days in human scale. But time is a relative phenomenon, as Einstein has proven to us, and our conception of time may be quite different from that conception by God on another scale. Poets have reminded us with similar metaphors that eons are less than eye-blinks on eternity's face. At such magnitudes time lies well beyond the pale of ordinary consciousness. Here the scientist shrugs his shoulder to the mystic but takes on the literalist with gusto. The fireworks have popped and fizzled for several centuries, with little enough illumination.

"I have said ... to the worm, Thou art my mother and my sister ... I am brother to dragons and a companion to owls."[3] These are words such as the racially arrogant of our species are likely to pass over with convenience. Yet they are from the Book of Job. This most ancient of the prophets obviously had ample time to consider his prebipedal ancestry and his living nonhuman relatives. Who will say that he did not know the reality of evolution in his mind and heart? This is the only understanding that diffuses the Darwinian bombshell, which all this time should have been no more than a small jolt to religious complacency.

Within the context of Eastern philosophy and spirituality, evolution and creation are compatible. In Sufism, for example, conventional religious terms are thought to symbolize the progress of the human mind from darkness to realization. Words such as "Adam and Eve," "grace," "angels," and "devil" are considered, after all, to be technical terms symbolic of internal, psychological processes. "Angel" and "devil," for example, are not literal forms, but are said to represent certain human mental faculties or propensities, with the latter representative of the lower self—animal tendencies, greed, prejudice and bigotry, overintellectualization, pedantry, and so on—and the former representative of the higher, spiritual self.

Numerous books have been written regarding the figurative interpretation of the Bible (and other forms of scripture, such as the Koran and the Vedas), some authored by well-known psychologists and philosophers, including Carl Jung (*Answer to Job*) and Maurice Nicoll (*The New Man*).

Another way of viewing the Bible is to consider it as divinely inspired but written by developed men for the purpose of helping the people to make better sense of their lives and to keep their lives in order. In other words, works like the Bible could be considered as temporary constructions adapted to the level of awareness of the people at the time. But like a scaffolding, once the overall awareness of the people had evolved to a higher stage, it might no longer be timely. Or something new might later be written (again, by persons divinely inspired), which could be adopted at the level of consciousness of the people at that time.

Any of these ideas or interpretations can help to reconcile religion with evolution, and the *issue* of religion (or creationism) *versus* evolution becomes a spurious one.

Nonetheless, creationism versus evolution is not the key issue of concern in this book. Creation/evolution has merely become a hot public issue to draw attention to scientists and religionists. And as the foregoing shows, the issue is easily resolved. In effect, the issue has clouded matters and has detracted from what ought to be our real concern: the fact that Darwinism (or the Darwinian theory of evolution) has thoroughly dominated our thought for the past 130 years and has crystallized into what is known as a Weltanschauung (from the German, meaning "world view"). Much like our ancient belief in the flatness of the earth, Darwinian evolution has almost totally eliminated all options.

Our thinking about evolution and the related matters of science, religion, spirituality, and human psychology is presently in need of reconsideration. The objective of this book is to provide some new perspectives on these matters, with due emphasis on the phenomenon of human evolution, its necessity and broad implications.

Chapter Two

PARADIGM SHIFT

Science is always wrong. It never solves a problem without creating ten more.

George Bernard Shaw

In the November 1981 issue of *Discover* magazine, the eminent biologist, Lewis Thomas, states,

> Evolution has long since passed the stage of theory. There can no longer be any question at all, in any educated mind, that the species in today's world evolved from precursor creatures in a line stretching all the way back to the bacteria-like fossils that have been found embedded in rocks laid down more than 3.5 billion years ago. Nor can the central role played by Darwinian natural selection be held in question. These are matters of scientific fact, as solid as any available to mankind.[1]

Darwinian theory, or dogma as its critics prefer, represents what scientists now refer to as a dominant paradigm. A paradigm (like "world view") is a framework of thought (from the Greek *paradigma*, "pattern") that tends to focus our attention in a certain direction or area of reality. The term was made popular in scientific circles by Thomas Kuhn in 1962, with the publication of his book *The Structure of Scientific Revolutions*. Using several well-known examples from the history of science, Kuhn emphasized that, although a scientific paradigm or "overriding theoretical framework" helps make experimental data more understandable and directs new research, it is also something that tends to resist change—even in the face of new data that do not "fit." Rather than having the dominant paradigm be questioned, the new information is usually either ignored or rejected outright.

Examples include the discovery that the earth circled the sun rather than the sun circling the earth, that the moon affected the tides, that space and time were the same, and that "solid" matter consisted mostly of empty space. Paralleling these discoveries were such paradigm shifts as the Copernican, Newtonian, and Einsteinian revolutions in science. According to Kuhn, paradigms are so slow to shift in the face of new evidence simply because scientists tend to *cherish* their theories—to invest a great deal of their *self-esteem* in their ideas (as do other people as well—but scientists are people too, aren't they?). Paradigms, then, tend to be revered, even worshipped subconsciously like religious tenets.

About the same time Kuhn's book was released, Arthur Koestler, working along independent lines, suggested much the same thing about paradigms in his book *The Act of Creation*. But Koestler took the issue beyond science and noticed the parallel in art as well as in the populace as a whole.

Koestler, in his recent book *Janus*, also describes the historic cycles or stages in which paradigms are built up and broken down. He points out that progress in human thought is of a pattern not unlike that of evolution: change is neither exclusively gradual or radical; instead, there is an ongoing alternation between the two. Koestler sees the dynamic, revolutionary phase as comparatively brief, a creatively chaotic period in which new hybrids of ideas (and species) are born. This is the prelude to much lengthier periods of more harmonious and quieter evolutionary labors, a time of "consolidating the new frontiers, or verifying, elaborating and extending the new synthesis."[2]

Koestler goes on to explain how the new synthesis eventually ossifies into unadaptability, deteriorates, and gives way to relatively rapid, unheaving change once again. The process continues thus, ad infinitum. Koestler refers to this developing entity as a "matrix," viewing the total process as organic growth, whether in art, science, or life itself.

In this light, Darwinism can be understood as a 19th-century paradigm, overdue for a shift into the 20th and 21st. When viewed through less blinkered eyes, it begins to be seen as a fossilized theory, integral in a limited way, but misplaced and misvalued. John C. Greene, in his book *Science, Ideology, and the World View*, takes the problem of the shifting paradigm into the broader context of culture and the general advance of human thought. Holding that the modern neo-Darwinists themselves (e.g., Edward O. Wilson, Theodosius Dobzhansky, George Gaylord Simpson) might need to admit that their scientific theories and writings are at best tenuously valid descriptions of phenomena, he concludes that the same kind of ideological influences (scientific, philosophical, sociocultural, etc.) found in Darwin's outlooks are also evident in the neo-Darwinists' writings and should therefore be regarded as not intellectually and scientifically objective in the true sense. Greene believes science is but one facet—albeit a necessary one—of humanity's overall comprehension of the universe and itself.[3]

In other words, science is not an absolute qualifier of reality, material or otherwise. As a description of reality it may be presently more useful than others for certain tasks (e.g., harnessing and exploring nature), but as a revealer of human meaning it is a mere toddler, albeit a precocious one, stumbling its way toward profundities reached by legitimate metaphysics and mysticism long ago. Here, however, contemporary thought reaches a philosophical fork in the road. While some scientists feel that their endeavors are modest contributions to a historical new synthesis of religion and science, others, such as the foregoing evolutionary biologists, believe their discipline to be the only one worthy of assuming the role of the New Myth. By their logic, "unscientific" religion, mysticism, and metaphysics are museum pieces.

The paradigm is shifting but has not yet established a direction. We experience the uncertainty in all areas of life and sense major changes in the offing. What has been called The Age of Anxiety may only be a foretaste of that change. However, it is best to remember that the collective spirit of the times, or *Zeitgeist*, can be any mixture of delusion, confusion, and enlightenment. These run in cycles similar to individual human moods and may affect the thinking of a "thinker" as much as anyone else's. Ideally, society should cope creatively with its problems and moods, just as the individual should. Maturation is thereby achieved, the measure of evolution. For those who can read it accurately, the *Zeitgeist* is the sign of the times that tells us whether our social thought is advancing by cycles or merely running in circles. The paradigm can be a merry-go-round.

Much modern thought, including neo-Darwinism, is made clearer within the context of the *Zeitgeist*. If we accept, for example, that the psychic maturation of the human race is far from completed, it is not hard to analogize our species as being in a stage of adolescence, sensing its real potential but still deeply unsure of itself emotionally and intellectually. It vacillates between its earlier impulses and egocentrism and the wise acknowledgment of its ignorance. Attempting to bridge the gaps of growing up, it rationalizes, it theorizes. It desperately needs guidance and is likely to seek it anywhere. Thus, in many ways we see the tragedy of youth in the present age of humanity. The sophistries of our theories must at last give way to the realization of our true state.

How the *Zeitgeist* works or why is still not totally understood. One of the better theories was suggested by the 17th-century Italian philosopher Giambattesta Vico. It was his feeling that historical events and trends in human thinking reflect a series of stages through which all human societies traverse. In his cyclical theory of history, he believed that all societies go through three stages, which are paralleled by three general stages of human development. He referred to these as the imaginative, the heroic, and the humanistic stages (or mentalities). He suggested that the basic human nature of any society went through a progression of stages similar to that which we would observe a child go through. The *imaginative* stage is marked by a set of beliefs determined by the use of vivid imagination. One of the main features of this age would be a pronounced belief in a world of gods, with social institutions and practices reflecting this. An example would be the beliefs of the early Romans and Greeks in their hierarchy of mythical gods. Vico also referred to this as the poetic or theological age. The *heroic* stage reflects the beginnings of the use of reason. Here, people try to make sense of things by way of reason but are, however, only partially successful. Their conception of God, for example, may enter into a realm of organized religion, and their educational system may become quite emphatic about logical analysis and detail; however, a more comprehensive, general approach is not yet possible. The *human or humanistic* stage is considered by Vico to be the final stage: people would at last be able to think clearly about the nature of things, and their social practices and institutions would reflect this.

So, in Vico's view, the stage of development that any given human culture or society has reached at any given time will supersede all else and largely determine what is or is not acceptable in the various fields of thought—for example, economic, artistic, scientific, political, spiritual.[4] This is especially obvious in the field of art, where artistic trends (impressionism, surrealism, etc.) parallel (or are slightly ahead of, but not too far ahead of) the mentality of the people. But this is not as obvious in the field of science. Yet the same process is equally evident there. As an example, let us consider the size of the sun and its distance from the earth. During the imaginative stage, relatively primitive peoples of all backgrounds will tend to view the sun as being, say, about the size of a gold coin and no farther away than the horizon. Certainly their scientists (i.e., their shamans) will rationalize a precise means of providing these well-established "facts." During the later stages of development, as scientific methods change, so will the society's views about the sun. During the heroic stage the sun, by way of questioning and some technological development, may come to be seen as further away and yet also—wrongly by this stage's standards—as revolving around the earth; "scientific" facts as to its size and distance will be in concordance.

Today, we believe scientists when they tell us that the sun is huge and incredibly hot and that it is 92 million miles away. It would be virtually unthinkable for any of us to doubt this fact. But then again, in the next century or two people may look back askance, thinking, "How strange ... how could they ever have believed that?" Although no one really knows what our 22nd century's scientific view of the sun will be, it is not inconceivable, say, that we might not view the sun as something "out there," but rather as something situated deep inside the brains of all of us. Concomitantly, our scientific knowledge of the human brain may have advanced to such a level that we might even be able to routinely travel to the sun (and beyond) merely by a specialized mental act of will (in fact sages and mystics claim that, with some people, this is possible even now).

The point here is that our opinions, beliefs, theories, views, and scientific facts are generally intertwined with the *Zeitgeist*, and they in large part may be considered as historically conditioned and not necessarily objective or unchangeable.

Returning to Lewis Thomas's assertion that opened this chapter, we may begin to understand that the idea of the "central role played by

Darwinian natural selection" may not be beyond question; we may especially question the statement, "These are matters of scientific fact, as solid as any available to mankind."

As the *Zeitgeist* changes, so do people's minds; as this begins to come about, the likelihood of the emergence of a new world view is thereby enhanced.

Chapter Three

PERSPECTIVE

Distance does not make you falter, now arriving in magic, flying, and, finally, insane for the light, you are the butterfly and you are gone.

And so long as you haven't experienced this: to die and so to grow, you are only a troubled guest on the dark earth.

Goethe

Although various scientists, scholars, and writers have taught that the decline of Christianity was primarily due to the influence of Darwin, the writer R.H. Barfield, in line with Vico, notes that the cause and effect of these phenomena were in reality the reverse; Darwinism in fact provided a secular belief system that filled the psychic void left by lost faith in Christian supernaturalism. Barfield buttresses this view by citing the Canadian biologist W. R. Thompson, who in his introduction to the "everyman" edition of Darwin's *Origin of Species* maintains that there is an ongoing natural appetite to replace the immaterialist concepts of religion with wholesale materialist ones.[1]

So the *Zeitgeist* from about 1860 to the present day has provided fertile soil for the implantation of Darwinian seed. Essentially, Darwinism has taken root during what Vico would refer to as the humanistic stage, a period in which religion was on the decline, with mass media, science, and technology coterminously on the rise. Interpreting Vico at the present time, we in the modern world are rapidly approaching the terminal phase of the humanistic stage. Holding a cyclical view of history, he believed that once man reached the final, third stage his questioning would continue until society could no longer hold him in check and he would soon rebel. He would soon realize that society was not created by gods, that very little was sacred, and subsequently his animal self would take over and undermine his socially conditioned self. This would reveal itself in demands for increasingly permissive forms of social behavior and morality, until the foundations of society, including morality (or the conception of right and wrong) would disappear. Since there would be nothing left to check his basic, anti-social drives, in due time wars would proliferate (primarily civil war) and all of man's social and cultural achievements would be obliterated. Humanity would be reduced to its initial state of bestiality, and the whole historical cycle would then start anew.

Although eminently reasonable, Vico's theory is still a pessimistic view. While we might wish to entertain Vico's views as a guide to our general understanding, a more optimistic view of human nature might assist in altering our overall perspective.

Knowledge gained from the ancient East, as well as recent research in human psychology, reveals that humans have potentials for higher development (beyond Vico's humanistic stage) that can be tapped and cultivated. This has been the subject of study for Dr. Maurice Bucke (discussed in his classic work *Cosmic Consciousness*, written in 1901) as well as for Abraham Maslow, the American psychologist. Both of these writers intensively researched the lives of exceptional people, past and present (e.g., Jesus, Mohammed, Buddha, Socrates, Bacon, Blake, Einstein, and others), and discovered that these persons not only excelled the norm but were living proof of man's ability to develop a "mystic relation to the Infinite." Recent discoveries in a branch of psychology known as transpersonal psychology have determined that most people have the potential for higher development, however few succeed at cultivating this capacity or even make the effort.

Unknown to Vico, certain ancient Eastern societies have transcended the cycle into a fourth stage, outside the confines of social conditioning. Instead of reverting to a more primitive level, these communities have moved several steps farther, into a realm that can best be described as an advanced level of human evolution.

Transpersonal psychology is presently attracting a great deal of interest, not only among psychologists, but among a significant sector of the populace as a whole. The current interest in human potential and the so-called "human growth movement" may be more than just another passing trend. If anything, surely it indicates (in line with the views of Kuhn, Koestler, and Greene) that should a considerable proportion of modern peoples or societies succeed at transcending the norm, then thinking would progress and increase in flexibility as well. This may be especially true in the area of evolutionary thinking, where Darwinism and its materialistic, mechanistic, reductionistic view of life and the human species is, like Vico's view, wholly pessimistic and more than likely in need of supersession.

Agreeing that we in the contemporary age are in a position to transcend our prior limitations, Henryk Skolimowski notes that

> science has recently transcended its mechanistic model. The story of science transcending itself is a magnificent manifestation of evolution's chief modus operandi—ceaseless and continuous transcendence. It is now up to us to allow our minds to transcend their mechanistic confines and other deterministic trappings in order to create a world view which at least would match the recent horizons of science.[2]

When Skolimowski refers to "science" he is basically referring to modern physics, where the Newtonian, mechanical/materialistic world view has given way to the Einsteinian relativistic world view. At the present time, physics has progressed far ahead of the general populace in its advanced ways of thinking and is even farther ahead in this respect than all of the other known sciences (except, perhaps, astronomy). However, "when we talk about science in the context of our civilization we invoke the image of an infallible deity. The sad truth is that the new outlook on the nature of science has not yet become a part of our new outlook on the world. It has not even penetrated deeply enough in our schools to prevent us from being brought up and educated, still, within the regime of 19th-century science."[3]

Nonetheless, we are undoubtedly at a crossroads in contemporary civilization, where, as Skolimowski reminds us, it is now up to us to transcend our ordinary ways of thinking.

Chapter Four

EVOLUTIONARY COMPREHENSION

Man descended from a fish in the beginning of the world.

Anaximander of Miletos
Sixth Century B.C.

I have been ere and now a boy and a girl, a bush and a bird and a dumb fish in the sea.

Empedokles
Fifth Century B.C.

The new-born Earth first flung up herbs and shrubs. Next in order it engendered the various breeds of mortal creatures, manifold in mode of origin as in form ... more and bigger ones took shape and developed ... first ... birds ... then ... mammals ...

Lucretius
First Century B.C.

The phenomenon or idea of evolution is one of the broadest and most wide-ranging concepts known to humanity. Webster's *New World Dictionary* notes some of the connotations associated with the word evolution:

> [L. *evolutio*, an unrolling or opening ...] 1. An unfolding, opening out, or working out; process of development, formation or growth. 2. A result or product of this; thing evolved. 3. a) A movement that is part of a series or pattern. b) A problem produced, or seemingly produced, by such a series of movements: as, the *evolutions* of a fancy skater. 4. A setting free; giving off; emission or disengaging....

Webster then goes on to define evolution in terms of biology, mathematics, and even the military. Though we normally associate the notion of evolution with science, biology, and Darwin, it is clear from Webster's delineation that evolution entails much more.

But science has fixated us upon its almost exclusive right to the investigation of evolution, and especially the theories of Darwin, albeit Skolimowski and others make it quite clear that evolution is a central, even eschatological concept, intuitively sensed by humankind as a force that drives it in diverse ways to better its state. It is realized by some people as a high, if hazy truth. As such it is timeless and cannot be proven by any single theory of science, since science itself is only one manifestation of it. The "blind men of Hindustan" cannot prove the reality of the elephant, even if the zoologist among them is able to break off part of a tusk to take home and analyze. More succinctly, a part cannot prove the whole.

Skolimowski notes that evolution (or the notion of evolution) precedes science, and in a sense even encompasses it. As such, it is a *frame* concept—that is, an intellectually total concept that encompasses even the definition and concerns of science. Moreover, evolutionary processes and thought are not accessible through strictly scientific language, since the latter is limited by its very quantitative definitions. Finite things and ideas cannot take in infinite ones, parts cannot encompass wholes. Therefore, evolution is not a "scientific" phenomenon, even though its local effects can be investigated by scientific methods. Skolimowski emphasizes, quite rightly, that "evolution precedes science. The process of evolution has generated the phenomenon of science, not the converse." At best, "we should simply acknowledge that the pursuit of science has made evolution conscious of itself." Yet it should not be overlooked that epistemological, philosophical, eschatological, and cosmic theories of evolution have also served this same end.[1]

Skolimowski also points out that while it is assumed that science is about reality, science actually deals in a particular class of *descriptions* of reality. Science cannot legitimately assume that it deals in reality or truth, but simply in its *version* of reality or truth. And then its versions are modified, or replaced with new versions, as it progresses.

Evolution must now be viewed as an immense and comprehensive phenomenon, influencing not only the behavior and physiology of plants, animals, and humans, but manifesting itself throughout the universe and at all levels, subatomic through galactic. Evolution also influences the development of our minds, something quite elusive to materialistically oriented scientists, and the notion of the evolution of consciousness must likewise be considered legitimate domain for investigation.

When we speak of evolution we may consider the evolutionary process at any level of analysis within the universe as we know it. The usual levels of analysis include: subatomic particles, atoms, molecules, cells, tissues, organs, organisms (plants, animals, humans), societies, planets, stars, galaxies, and metagalaxies. These are somewhat arbitrary divisions; however, they are commonly used and can serve as a useful frame of reference.

Since the universe includes everything and anything, known or unknown, visible and invisible, we know little about how it came into existence. Various scientists, however, have attempted to explain how the visible or physical universe came into being. Currently, the most popular scientific theory is known as the Friedmann-Gamov general astrophysical model of the "big bang" universe, or simply, the Big Bang Theory. The theory claims that at some time, long ago, all matter in the universe was located in one compact, hot ball of huge density. One writer, Itzhak Bentov (*Stalking the Wild Pendulum*) refers to this hot ball as "... a kind of cosmic egg with all matter and space in it."[2] Then this egg somehow began to expand and explode. This explosion, or "big bang," is thought to have been everywhere concentric and uniform, so that matter and space began to expand equally in all directions. Initially, the matter was of very high-temperature, high-frequency radiation and, as it expanded, it began to gradually cool until larger, stable compounds began to form. Neutrons, electrons, and protons made their appearance in what we know as solid matter. In this hot "particle soup" the simple elements were formed.[3] These included the most primitive, the hydrogen and helium atoms. These formed immense clouds known as nebulae, which started breaking down into smaller subunits. Due to their own gravitational pull these began to condense, thereby forming a basis for evolving galaxies. The first stars were thought to appear in the form of "blobs of hydrogen gas." With time, very high temperatures formed at the core of these blobs or stars. These temperatures rose, until they began to create nuclear reactions. These nuclear reactions produced a great amount of heat and light; and then the first heavenly bodies, like our sun, were born. The elemental ingredients that make up our own physical bodies were built up in the searing interior of these stars, the "star stuff" in fact of all earthly life.[4]

Big Bang theorists assume that, since the time of the initial big explosion, all matter has become distributed as if it were on the surface of an ever-expanding balloon. Evidence for this assumption is available, since astronomers and astrophysicists tell us that when we look at distant galaxies through our telescopes they appear to be "running away from each other," moving further and further out into space. The volume of our physical universe is continually increasing, and this is why we refer to it as the "expanding [or evolving] universe." Bentov speculates that at some point in future time this expansion might stop and reverse or contract itself— thus the idea of a "pulsating universe."

As the universe expands it is opposed by one mighty force, gravity. Gravity links together all the hurling fragments from the initial explosion so that they comprise a supergalactic system, insead of flinging haphazardly out in all directions of space. Should gravity succeed in stopping the expansion so that all matter and energy returned into one single, compressed ball, as some scientists predict, then all creation may become annihilated. This is referred to as the "Antibang." But then, the writer Malcolm Ross MacDonald speculates that this 80-billion-year Bang cycle may be but a local ripple in a yet vaster "superuniverse," and our detectable universe an undistinguished backwater in the larger cosmos. Rather resignedly, he concludes that "beyond the limits of time and space there is, for us, only silence."[5]

Our own galaxy, the Milky Way, is estimated by scientists to have formed about 10 billion years ago. It is thought that about once every century a star will die (while others will be born). Stars typically die a violent death in what is referred to as a supernova explosion. A star collapses and explodes as the result of extreme inward pressure caused by gravity. The star's interior burns quickly at very high temperatures (hundreds of millions of degrees), and at this temperature it is thought that its protons, neutrons, and electrons can combine to form the 92 elements. Supernova explosions served to scatter these elements throughout the galaxy, with about 93 percent being hydrogen, about 6 percent helium, and the last 1 percent comprising all the other 90 elements (carbon, oxygen, iron, aluminum, etc.). The combinatory abilities of the atoms actualize the material world as we know it: hydrogen combines with oxygen to make water; oxygen combines with iron, aluminum, and silicon to make the various kinds of rocks, and so on.[6] The atoms combined by sharing their electrons. With water, for example, the electrons that spin around two hydrogen nuclei also make orbits around an oxygen nucleus, thereby creating a "package" tied together with a "blur of electronic string" (H_2O). Hydrogen, oxygen, nitrogen, and carbon combined to make a glycine molecule, the simplest amino acid, which all organisms contain.

The most widely accepted model of star formation has it that our star, the sun, was born about 5 billion years ago. Merely an ordinary star in our vast galaxy, the sun is 860,000 miles in diameter and continually radiates 370,000 billion billion kilowatts of energy out into space, with our earth absorbing only one two-billionth part of that energy (two million times the current energy requirements of humankind). The planets that rotate around the sun formed from heavy elements in its vicinity; the heaviest of these elements gathered into solid matter (dust), the dust turned into grains, the grains into pebbles, the pebbles into boulders. Some of these boulders may have been the size of mountains, which over time converged at varying distances from the sun, collapsing on one another under gravitation and eventually forming into larger bodies—the planets of our present solar system. Of all the planets in our solar system, it is believed that only the earth can support life as we know it, simply because it is situated at just the right distance from the sun. If a planet is too near the sun its atmosphere boils off into space, while if it is too far away its atmosphere will freeze.

The earth is thought to be about 4.6 billion years old. As mentioned, it is believed to have begun with the convergence of cold dust, pebbles, and boulders. As they crashed together and grew into a greater mass, the friction of their contact produced a great deal of heat. Locked deep inside this growing mass were atoms of thorium, radium, and uranium—large, unstable atoms that can split up spontaneously, releasing vast amounts of nuclear energy. This energy, trapped deep inside the ever-growing earth, began to heat up from within. Eventually, the outer skin of the earth cracked under this internal pressure, releasing (in the form of volcanoes) gases of various sorts, such as methane (made from carbon and hydrogen), ammonia (from nitrogen and hydrogen), carbon dioxide (carbon and oxygen), and water (in the form of steam). With these vital elements being released into the surrounding atmosphere, and with the steam being condensed into clouds, and the clouds condensing into raindrops, the stage was set for the beginnings of life. So much watery steam was released into the atmosphere, and for such a long period of time, that it is thought that it rained on earth ceaselessly for several millennia (the Great Flood?), thereby creating the lakes, seas, and oceans.

Life began in the seas. Over vast periods of time storms raged, lightning flashed, and the sun produced heat and light. As the warm water from the oceans evaporated, clouds formed that drenched the lands with rain. The thunderbolts were accompanied by high-energy radiation that collided and melded simple molecules into larger ones in the tenuous and noxious atmosphere of water vapor, methane, ammonia, and carbon dioxide. These molecules contained the ingredients of the "soup" of life that was thus poured into the seas. Amino acids, fatty lipids, nucleotide bases, and phosphates (which combine with sugar to form sugar-phosphates) are the primary constituents of each living organism on earth, making every plant, animal, and human a close relative of every other—and a distant relative of every rock and clod of earth.

Amino acids activated by energy from the atmosphere behaved like magnets, snapping together to form lines, called proteins. Sugar-phosphates clipped themselves together with combinations of the four nucleotide bases, forming chains known as nucleotide acids. Eventually, one chain of nucleic acids formed into a double chain, giving birth to the first strands to become known as DNA (deoxyribonucleic acid). DNA soon began to develop the ability to unzip and automatically form indentical copies of itself from the nucleotides around it (RNA, ribonucleic acid). In parallel fashion, amino acids began to join up with other amino acids, forming larger clusters. Through mutual cooperation, DNA/RNA, amino acids, and proteins (as well as other organic molecules) began to form self-replicating life forms. New and different life forms could evolve simply by variations occurring along the lines of self-replicating DNA.

Soon certain primitive living cells were formed, known today as bacteria. Plant cells were formed when the first cells—blue-green algae, at least 2.5 billion years ago—made pigments to protect themselves from the sun's harmful ultraviolet radiation; this pigment, green in color, is known as chlorophyll. Chlorophyll is very special, as it is able to turn sunlight into energy—a form of electrical energy. With chlorophyll, cells are able to take in molecules of carbon dioxide and water to create molecules of sugar, a rich energy source. The byproduct of this chemical interaction is oxygen, the key constituent in air and the major source of sustenance (along with food) of practically all forms of life that have evolved and/or are in existence to this day.

Single-cell organisms mostly reproduce by fission, or splitting. The next major evolutionary breakthrough was the development of division of labor between cells—the multicellular organism. Whereas the DNA content (genes) is identical in every cell of multicellular organisms, the division of labor or the specialization of cells is effected by a selective turning on or off of specific genes in the total complex of genes (genome). Some cells organize to become the circulatory system (heart, blood, etc.), others the muscular system, the skeleton, the nervous system, and so forth.

Instead of asexual fission for purposes of reproduction, some single-celled species began to evolve genders, resulting in sexual reproduction. Certain multicellular organisms evolved a more elaborate reproductive system, comprised of a new organization of specialized sexual cells, or the gametes: sperm and egg. After plants, swimming plant/animals evolved. These were followed by various forms of simple invertebrates, fish, then amphibians (water/land animals). The march of evolution on land began: insects, reptiles, birds, dinosaurs, primitive mammals. Finally the primates appeared, leading to prehistoric humans/apes, the primitive human and modern human.

All along, and simultaneously, the earth itself was evolving. Early on, about 140 million years ago, there was a single earthian land mass, now known as Pangea. Pressures underneath its crust began to pull it apart, and about 65 million years ago Pangea then split into two, Lourasia in the north and Gondwanaland in the south. Gondwanaland subsequently split up into what geologists refer to as "plates," which included South America, Africa, India, Antarctica/Australia. North America split from Europe/Asia about 60 to 65 million years ago. Later the Indian plate collided with the Eurasian, pushing up the Himalayas. The Australian and Antarctican plates separated, North and South America united, while the African plate joined with the Eurasian plate. The various seas and oceans took up their present positions as did the valleys and mountains. These convergent geologic developments also produced alterations in climatic conditions. And all the while these various changing conditions assisted in the evolution of new life forms. DNA inside every cell of every life form transmuted in parallel with these evolutionary changes, thus resulting in the great diversity of life found everywhere on earth to this day.

Chapter Five

HUMAN ORIGINS

*Humanity under the influence of such events as wars,
or as a result of the necessity to adapt itself to the
changes brought about by mechanical progress and the
ensuing social problems, reacts violently by twists of
the helm which seem to carry it far from its course. But
the transcendent laws it unknowingly obeys have
brought it in less than a thousand centuries to its present state and scorn these ephemeral digressions which
become imperceptible on the scale of evolution.*

Lecomte DuNoüy,
Human Destiny

Undeniable scientific evidence of the evolution of human culture and civilization provides strong logical and analogical support for the mental and physical evolution of the human species. It is known, for instance, that the brain's neural mass increases with ongoing problem-solving activity, long after achieving chronological maturation. This knowledge fits well with the generally accepted theory of our human ancestors' migration from arboreal habitations to savannah environments. Long-distance viewing of potential danger or sources of food and protection would require the more or less erect posture not demanded of them as tree-dwellers. In addition, and no less important, life on the grasslands would require new, more complex survival strategies (tool and weapon making, social reorganization, etc.) that would in turn stimulate brain growth.

But it is not only paleoanthropological research that lends considerable collateral support for the morphological and mental evolution of humankind; serological (blood) analysis also adds credibility to the various hypotheses of our primate origins, as shown by the chromosomal or genetic commonalities that certain simian species share with our own. The closest of these is the chimpanzee, whose blood constituency is 98 percent identical to *Homo sapiens*.

As mentioned earlier, there is no rational need for the either/or creationist-evolutionist argument, provided that (1) Darwinism as *theory* is distinguished from evolutionary *evidence* per se, and (2) religious texts be interpreted allegorically rather than literally. Hence, in the latter case Adam and Eve may be taken as symbolic of the phylogenetic transition from animal to human and/or representing higher ontogenetic mental development. Similarly, the story of Noah, the Ark, and the Great Flood can be seen as the respective metaphors of *humankind* in the crisis of survival, *knowledge* that will ensure not only its survival but its prevalence, in the midst of the engulfing perils of the *world*. Unyieldingly literal interpretation of such narratives diminishes them as vehicles of inner understanding and, in some cases, reduces them to absurdity (typified by the two Christian scholars who assert the exact physical dimensions of the Ark as "437.5 feet in length, 72.92 feet in width, and 43.75 feet in height").[1]

Something like this same kind of errant penchant for particularizing broad, universal truths into temporal specificity is also displayed in the frequent quibbling of the paleoanthropologists as to whether the first true human-ape was, for example, *Ramapithecus* (12 million years ago) or *Australopithecus* (5 million years ago). All too much attention has been fixed on this issue. Whenever a new variation of old bones is unearthed, the anatomical evolutionists whip up the scientific atmosphere with yet another round of bone-splitting debate, usually aired *ad summum* throughout the media. Such was the recent stir generated by the discovery of "Lucy," thought to be a later form of *Australopithecus*.

Essentially, the transition to human is chronologically an extremely lengthy one, having occurred over several millions of years. The first skull to be described as "basically human" is known as *Homo habilis*, dating back about 2 million years. From this line developed the species *Homo erectus*, extant around 1 million years later. *H. erectus* had a comparatively large cranium (hence a large brain) and was a highly successful and populous forerunner of modern man. Its direct descendent was *Homo sapiens neanderthalis* (100,000 years ago) and *Homo sapiens sapiens* (appearing 50,000 years ago with Cro-Magnon man, whose fossil remains are almost identical with those of people today).

Archeological evidence, as well as findings from ethology, comparative anatomy, and psychology, makes a near airtight case for our earliest anthropoid ancestors' forest existence. As prehumans ventured down out of the trees their bipedal capabilities began to develop, and they were able to supplement their diet with new nutrients obtained by ground feeding.

The transformation of *Homo habilis* into *Homo erectus* entailed a series of significant, if not dramatic, coordinated developments. Our ancestors' accelerating bipedal abilities were a function of the continually increasing erectility of their anatomy. Their array of tools and weapons expanded generally with their larger brain mass. As Desmond Morris notes in *The Naked Ape*, these developments came about not in simple cause-effect sequences, but manifested in integrated sets, one advance reinforcing and being reinforced by others in a subtle dynamic, "each urging the other on ... a hunter ape, a killer ape, in the making."[2]

A hunting livelihood required new forms of social cohesion among the hominoids. Hunting in packs, they were forced to evolve more effective and advanced modes of group communication, especially vocal, and group organization. Their ground existence presented whole new problems of survival; nonetheless they effectively met these challenges with new solutions, stimulating their brains into further growth.

Though the Neanderthals and Cro-Magnons were primarily cave dwellers, they constructed huts where natural lairs were not to be found, thus initiating additional demands upon the spatial (or patterning) and logical functions of their brains, undoubtedly an important impetus to right/left brain specialization. Seminal experiments in art and technology were made about this time, such as the renowned cave paintings, bodily adornment, innovations of tools and weaponry, firemaking, and the construction of hearths. Interestingly, however, we know relatively little about the intervening cultures between Cro-Magnon and the beginnings of the well-documented Middle and Far Eastern civilizations that appeared roughly 10,000 years ago. This incredible quantum gap in our anthropology covering several thousands of years is a mysteriously missing chapter in human history. Since Cro-Magnon was anatomically nearly identical to the modern human, we might expect these shadowy millennia to be tremendously transitional epochs, with momentous strides forward in technical and mental advancement ushering in greater understanding of the world.

Unfortunately, all that is available to us are legends of these veritable "missing links" in the evolving network of civilization. One exception is the series of recent discoveries dating the existence of North American hunting tribes at 19,000 B.C. These groups might comprise the pieces of a larger puzzle centering on the mythical lost continent of Atlantis, which some geologists concur sank to the bottom of the Atlantic Ocean approximately 10,000 years ago. Many respected historians and anthropologists theorize that this huge island-continent supported a highly advanced culture that propagated the later major civilizations on both sides of the Atlantic. The striking similarities between much of the science, art, and religion of Native American and Middle Eastern culture is explained by such a theory, buttressed as it is by impressive archeological analysis.

Prior to about 10,000 years ago, hunting and gathering were the two major means of obtaining food. Then humans, by chance or experiment, learned that certain edible plants could be seeded and cultivated, and the agricultural revolution began. Just as their descent from the trees prompted the first wave of developments and adaptations, so did their exit from the caves and communal crop-tending pave the way for a yet higher order of discovery and achievement. Obviating the need for roaming and foraging, a farming culture creates surplus time (given surplus harvest), perpetuating a more sedentary lifestyle. Prehistoric humans found themselves with time on their hands. And since an agricultural economy can support a much denser population than a hunting/gathering one, villages, towns, and cities inevitably sprang forth from the primitive bands of soil tillers. Communal life continued to accelerate in technical and social complexity.

Accompanying this remarkable stage of cultural advancement and sophistication over the past 5000 or so years, excessive aggression and violence color an unhappily dark side to the human story (e.g., war and crime). Although some writers (Konrad Lorenz, Robert Ardrey, Desmond Morris, etc.) believe that human nature is essentially—and perhaps indelibly—aggressive, others (like Richard Leakey) contend that its cooperative and pacific attributes are just as basic. There is ample evidence to support both views. And in fact, humanity's genetic heritage is in all probability dual-natured in this regard, one or the other tendency dominating according to environmental and social conditions. Above all, the species *Homo sapiens* is creative and possesses a vast capacity to learn.

The birth of historical civilization is usually slotted at about 4000 B.C., with the advent of the Egyptian and Sumerian cultures. Prodigious strides were made in this Middle Eastern arena, affecting all facets of life— religion, science, the arts, philosophy, and government. The Chinese, Greeks, Romans, Arabs, Africans, Asiatics, Spaniards, Japanese, Scandinavians, Europeans, and other groups advanced civilization into the modern age. An interesting footnote to these formidable chapters of history are a number of ancient tribes variously located around the globe who were geographically isolated from the greater cultural tides, maintaining a relatively static and primitive existence for centuries.

Today we may be on the brink of a third major thrust (after the Industrial Age) into humanity's evolutionary future. The computer-robot and other advanced technologies are releasing even more of our time and energy for yet more advanced physical and mental ventures. The human mind, like nature, seems to abhor a vacuum and, just as civilization blossomed with the agricultural revolution, so a new evolutionary leap is likely being prepared for with the robotics revolution.

Though contemporary science continues to expand its understanding of human evolution, its deeper comprehension of the phenomenon has at the same time been delimited by its essentially materialistic outlook and method. Bones, fossils, artifacts, comparative anatomy, blood analysis, ethological observation, and genetic studies are sources of extremely valuable data, but the Darwinian exclusion of mind and consciousness leaves the body of evolutionary theory without a real head.

But the inadequacies of neo-Darwinist theory have yet to be fully recognized, and they are legion, as we will now see.

Chapter Six

DARWINISM

I am well aware that there is scarcely a single point discussed in this volume on which facts cannot be adduced, often apparently leading to conclusions directly opposite to those at which I have arrived. A fair result could be obtained only by fully stating and balancing the facts on both sides of each question, and this cannot possibly be here done.

Charles Darwin
Introduction,
The Origin of Species

One gets the impression that before that dapper gentleman Charles Darwin came along, all learned people of the world ran around muttering about Adam and Eve (or the "Biblical Bang Theory") and ignoring the scientific facts or even simple observations around them. Not so.

> First he appeared in the class of inorganic things,
> Next he passed therefrom into that of plants.
> For years he lived as one of the plants,
> Remembering naught of his inorganic state
> so different;
> And when he passed from the vegetive to
> the animal state
> He had no remembrance of his state as a plant,
> Except the inclination he felt to the world of plants,
> Especially at the time of spring and sweet flowers.
> Like the inclinations of infants towards their mothers,
> Which know not the cause of their
> inclination to the breast,
> Or the excessive inclination of young disciples
> Towards their noble and illustrious teachers....
>
> Again the great Creator, as you know,
> Drew men out of the animal into the human state.
> Thus man passed from one order of nature
> to another.
> Till he became wise and knowing and strong as
> he is now.[1]

These words of Rumi the Persian, taken from his *Masnavi*, were written in the 13th century, 600 years before Darwin and when he was still only a gleam in his ancestors' stamens and pistils.

The theory of evolution did not originate with Darwin. In fact, at the same time he was developing his ideas, the same theory was already independently being formulated by Alfred Russell Wallace. The first public unveiling of the theory of evolution by natural selection was a joint communication to the Linnaean Society by Darwin and Wallace in 1858.

Actually, Darwin's main contribution was not so much the originality of his theory, but the fact that he was the first to scientifically and systematically assemble and organize the *evidence* that established the reality of evolution.

A major error in scientific and public thinking has been the failure to separate Darwin's theories from his findings. Since his findings were so overwhelming, the tendency has been to consider his theory as equally overwhelming. And the creationism versus evolution issue further detracted from this key distinction.

Theodore Roszak and other prominent humanists recall how in high school and college they were taught to learn their Darwinism as devoutly as their theological peers learned religious dogma. "I learned it," he states, "as dogmatic truth, as I might have learned a religious catechism." He adds that, although physical evidence for Darwinist theory was set forth, there was no critique of the theory as a theory, alternative hypotheses were not seriously presented, and if a person was not a Darwinist it was automatically assumed he was a biblical fundamentalist.[2]

Roszak finds some irony in this, since several of Darwin's detractors in his own time successfully sidetracked his logic at key points, well before his later supporters stoked it up to a full head of steam. One of these was the doughty Bishop Wilberforce, maligned as an anti-intellectual because of his modest references to scripture. Although Wilberforce was indeed no mental wizard, he was not a fevered Bible-thumper either, and his arguments were respectably reasonable, remaining so today. These centered on anatomical criticisms of Darwin's morphological conclusions, evidently borrowed from the anatomist Richard Owen.[3]

So it is important to keep in mind that, though Darwin's *evidence* for evolution is sound, this must be separated from his *theory* attempting to account for this evidence, which may not be so sound.

The main premises of Darwinian (and neo-Darwinian) theory will be reviewed here, with a brief history of its development and widespread acceptance. Since *The Origin of Species* (first printed in 1859), Darwinian theory has undergone four eras of development up to the present: classical Darwinism, neo-Darwinism, the synthetic theory, and ultra-Darwinism (sociobiology and macroevolution).

CLASSICAL DARWINISM

The era following publication of *The Origin of Species* in 1859, in which Darwin's ideas were originally promulgated, comprises the period of classical Darwinism. It lasted until about 1900 (when neo-Darwinist ideas began to take effect). The key concepts in Darwin's original theory are: variability, natural selection, randomness, adaptability, fecundity, and acquired characteristics.

One of Darwin's earliest observations was to note the natural variability of organisms within a given species. This variability can be viewed as *phenotypical* (external, anatomical) as well as *genotypical* (genetic variation). Darwin was mainly referring to a phenotypic variation at the time. The significance of variability is understood in light of Darwin's key idea, that of natural selection, which comes from what

Darwin referred to as "man's selection," or the selective breeding of domestic animals (cows, chickens, horses, dogs, etc.) for favored features or traits. By *natural* selection, he meant that certain natural principles guided the selection of favored traits within a given species. And this selection was possible because of variability. For example, in the history of the horse species, certain horses ran faster than other horses and, since the faster horses could escape predators more readily, they were more likely to survive and, hence, produce offspring. In this way, through natural selection, or "natural breeding," the "survival of the fittest" was considered the rule determining a particular feature (such as running speed).

Though Darwin saw life as evolving by blood, sweat, and conflict, his concept of natural selection through the "survival of the fittest" was intellectually far distant from our present-day crude conception of "the law of the jungle." Born and bred a provincial gentleman, he was by temperament not fond of his tooth-and-nail vision of creation. Indeed, in a number of passages throughout *The Origin of Species* his tone is that of one wanting to avert his eyes from the unpleasantness he was so faithfully recording. But as a dedicated scholar, he could not. He would see the full complexity of natural selection and set it down truthfully. He would be a reporter rather than a prophet (although his latter-day adherents would insist on making him one). It is this faithfulness to his mission that drove him to seek out and extrapolate his subject to a plausible truth. Above all he strove to be logical.

But Darwin's logic faces extinction at points, as when, after describing the dynamically complex interplay of trait variability and environmental change that eliminates many species and perpetuates some, he finds instances (such as on the Gallapagos Islands) in which the process, due to environmental stasis and apparent inertia of whole species, has ground to a curious, nonevolutionary halt. What we are left with is a suspended animation of forms, either short- or long-term. The description, like the landscape, is foggy.

> Variations neither useful nor injurious would be affected by natural selection, and would be left either a fluctuating element, as perhaps we see in certain polymorphic species, or would ultimately become fixed, owing to the nature of the organism and the nature of the conditions.[4]

This is not the language of concise science, even theoretical. The words are from *The Origin of Species*, which was only a sketch of the later superstructure of *The Descent of Man*, but it is typical of much of the insubstantiality of the theory's foundation.

Darwin obviously believed that evolution takes an occasional break from its labors, such as in places like the Gallapagos, and nothing much will develop in these isolated locales, at least until the next earthquake or volcano. He evidently had small faith that lazy life could overcome its inertia without regular thrashings from the environment, and in that he may have been more of a country parson than he knew.

On the other hand the parson allowed that pangenerational (but for him peripheral) traits continually developed in organisms over long periods of time as the result of habit, independently of external events. An example that Darwin describes in his *Origin* is that of domestic animals with drooping ears; he noted "the view which has been suggested that the drooping is due to disuse of the muscles of the ear, from the animal being seldom much alarmed."[5] This idea, called "the inheritance of acquired characteristics," was not original but came from Jean Baptiste Lamarck in 1809. Darwin interpreted it as only supplementary to his theory of natural selection, where "Lamarckian" alterations of anatomy and physiology would merely subserve the established qualities of adaptation, which were produced solely by random conditions, that is, chance occurrences of place and time.

In Darwinian terms, therefore, randomness meant simple fortuity; a set of circumstances favorable or unfavorable for adaptation and survival. The main elements of the set were fecundity (increasing the species' odds for survival by sheer numbers), environmental-climatic stresses, and trait flexibility in responding to the stress over several generations. This idea of acquired characteristics was thrown out by the neo-Darwinists in the early 19th century as nonessential and detracting from the essence of the theory. Years later when the concept was revived, it was attacked even more virulently as falsehood and heresy.

NEO-DARWINISM

According to Darwin's rationale, new species emerged over long spans of time by the relentless operation of natural selection. But there was a problem with this, a missing factor. What was the *mechanism* that actually gave birth to new species? Even the environmental sleuths, the neo-Darwinists, were sure they could find the singular clue in some covert source outside the organism. But no such singularity was forthcoming until the discovery of radiation by the Curies in 1898. Melded with findings of a certain Augustine monk and botanist named Gregor Mendel in 1865 (and rediscovered thirty-five years later, after being virtually ignored), radiation was theoretical manna from heaven for evolutionists.

Radiation seemed to be randomness par excellence, since it was traceless and obeyed no known laws of earthly physics. It could also reach inside the gene and alter its material (the alteration known as a "mutation"). In the interim between the radiation strikes, genes did not change. Neither did genes ever interact to blend new characteristics— or so concluded Mendel in his paper entitled "Experiments in Plant Hybridization."

Mendel's term for gene was "unit of heredity," which, through his experiments with hybrid garden peas, he saw as the ultimate component of genetic structure. Such units were theoretical invisibilities, but they could explain the very visible differences in size, shape, and coloration of pea strains over successive generations. These differences were sharply polarized (no perceivable blendings or "compromises") and alternated regularly throughout the development of new strains. However, the ratio was always heavily in favor of one trait appearing over its alternative, and "dominant" and "recessive" genes entered the evolutionary arena.

Darwinian theory pushed into the 20th century and survived, even flourished, by combining two otherwise productive scientific discoveries in an easy, reductive juggling act that excluded other possibilities out of hand. Randomness was a steamroller that greatly appealed to the more mechanistic theorists because it didn't stop for the (to them) obstructive thoughts of as yet unseen functions and designs in nature. Such unanswered questions had been among the preoccupations of Lamarck, and the neo-Darwinists never ceased to shovel them under as ridiculous whenever pro-Lamarckians brought them up. Any new discovery that could be construed as supportive of randomness was offered up as solid evidence for it. Cosmic rays, microscopic lesions, undirected chemical or micromechanical shocks—such things appeared to be the very stuff of chance. And they were just a few of the unpredictables in nature.

These unpredictables assisted in the production of accidental mutations. Accidental mutation, then, was considered the physiological mechanism allowing for organic evolution. And although most mutations are deleterious, it was assumed by neo-Darwinists that an occasional one was adaptive and was favored by natural selection.

The schism between the neo-Darwinists and Lamarckians was further perpetuated by Dr. August Weismann, when in 1855 he propounded his doctrine of the "continuity and unalterability of the germ-plasm." In this view the gonads (which contain the "germ-plasm") are an isolated system—separate from the body (i.e., the "soma-cells"). Because of this imputed isolation, apparently no acquired characteristic could penetrate the "barrier," as Weismann called it—therefore (*ipso facto*) Lamarckism was an impossibility. This doctrine was perpetuated in the mid-20th century by Watson and Crick's central dogma holding that the DNA chains of heredity in the chromosomes are isolated from the rest of the body and passed on, in unaltered form, from generation to generation (unless, of course, some radiation intervenes to cause an accidental alteration).[6]

Following Weismann (as well as Hugo deVries of Holland, in the late 1800s), neo-Darwinism was later bolstered by the statistician Ronald A. Fisher in his book *The Genetical Theory of Natural Selection* (1929). It received added impetus from H. G. Wells, Julian Huxley, and G. P. Wells (*The Science of Life*, 1929), and from Thomas Hunt Morgan in his book *The Scientific Basis of Evolution* (1932).

THE SYNTHETIC THEORY

Synthetic theory pertains to the neo-Darwinian synthesis of natural selection with random mutation to form the basis for a revised theory of evolution. Although there really is no distinction between neo-Darwinism and synthetic theory, the latter term was taken up at a later date and describes neo-Darwinism in the modern era from about 1935 to the present. (The name "synthetic theory" was first coined in 1942 by J. S. Huxley in his book *Evolution: The Modern Synthesis*. Two classics on the theory are *Genetics and the Origin of Species* by Theodosious Dobzhansky, 1937 and 1951, and *The Major Features of Evolution* by G. G. Simpson, 1953.) Synthetic theory also refers to contemporary refinements and developments in standard neo-Darwinian concepts and claims.

Two of the clearest contemporary summaries of the synthetic theory (for the layperson) are contained in a chapter entitled "The Relevant Principles of Population Biology" by Edward O. Wilson in his book *Sociobiology* (1975),[7] and in a chapter titled "How It Works: Evolution as a Process," in *Sociobiology and Behavior* by David P. Barash (1977).[8]

The synthetic theory is primarily founded upon the neo-Darwinian premises of classical Darwinism (natural selection, fecundity, variability, etc.) and upon random mutationism. Another process believed important in evolution is that of sexual recombination, or the reshuffling of chromosomes that occurs every time eggs and sperm are produced. Hence, mutation and recombination may be considered the ultimate sources of genetic diversity, which in turn are operated upon by natural selection. (In a recent *Scientific American* paper titled "The Neutral Theory of Molecular Evolution," Motoo Kimura suggests that *genetic drift* may be even more important in evolution than selection, especially at the genotypic level.[9] Genetic drift is defined as "evolution, or change in the gene frequencies, by chance processes alone." Although this definition, which is taken from Edward O. Wilson's book *Sociobiology*, may seem circular, and hence questionable, a current controversy in biological science is nonetheless known as the "neutralist versus selectionist" debate.)

Building upon the basic neo-Darwinian premises, numerous other ideas have been furnished to buttress the synthetic theory. These include miscellaneous research concepts, statistical factors, and ideas from ancillary branches of population genetics and biology, all of which may be considered as corollaries to the basic Darwinian assumptions and tenets. To provide you a glimpse of the overwhelming number of supportive corollaries that have been accumulated, some of them are listed here (after Wilson) by terminology only:[10]

> *Microevolution*, which includes the Hardy-Weinberg law and concepts like mutation pressure, segregation distortion, genetic drift, gene flow and selection
>
> *Pheno-deviants* and *genetic assimilation*
>
> *Inbreeding and kinship*, which include the following ideas from population genetics: inbreeding coefficient of kinship (also called the coefficient of consanguinity), coefficient of relationship, and a statistical term, *path analysis*
>
> *Assortative and disassociative mating*, including homogamy
>
> *Population growth* (and its many statistical analyses)
>
> *Density dependence*, including reference to emigration, stress and endocrine exhaustion, reduced fertility, infortitude and cannibalism, competition, predation and disease, and social convention and epideictic displays
>
> *Intercompensation*
>
> *Population cycles of mammals*
>
> *Life tables* (and accompanying statistics)
>
> *Stable age distribution*
>
> *Reproductive effort*
>
> *r and K selection* (with their many correlates, including climate, mortality, length of life, etc.)

Very impressive. Perhaps too impressive? The mark of a good theory is its simplicity; with all of the synthetic theory's premises, corollaries, and subcorollaries, one might suspect something to be amiss here.

ULTRA-DARWINISM

Since Darwinism and neo-Darwinism are based upon questionable premises (as will be shown in the next chapter), synthetic theory can be seen as a futile attempt at ballasting a sinking ship. Although not fully realizing their situation, the most contemporary—and in some respects the most radical—theorists are nonetheless sensing a need to submit the synthetic theory to even more revision and alteration.

Ultra-Darwinism represents the frontier era. Its key ideas (in addition to the synthetic theory) include sociobiology and the theory of macroevolution.

Sociobiology was the term first coined by Edward O. Wilson in his book of the same name, originally published in 1975. Its impetus began with the disturbing finding (to Darwinists) that in practically all animal societies there exists the phenomenon of *altruism*, a process which, at first thought, seems to violate the principle of survival of the fittest. In altruism an individual sacrifices its own welfare for the purpose of assisting others (usually other members of its own species).

Wilson and his followers, providing the respectable term of "reciprocal altruism" to this Good Samaritan behavior, have been able to account for this seeming violation of Darwinian principles by considering it as in fact *another instance* of the principle of survival of the fittest. By a subtle sleight of mind, they have merely shifted our attention from the survival of the individual to survival of the group or species as a whole. In their view, the group as a whole is more significant in the process of evolution and evolutionary history than the mere individual.

Stretching this line of reasoning into speculative thinness, Wilson suggests that certain social deviations historically tabooed are being increasingly tolerated, even accepted, because of their new biological advantage to the race as a whole. One such example (cited in his book *On Human Nature*) is homosexuality, which, practiced on a large scale, would obviously be useful in population control. He argues that mass biology has always created mass value but that altruistic man has simply never recognized that his selflessness is in his genes and his basic impulses. Here the "pleasure principle" picks up a little support through inverted logic. It is sociobiological theory at its shell-game best.

Sociobiology is defined as the "systematic study of the biological basis of all social behavior." Its basic premise is that most social behavior is primarily rooted in hereditary, developmental, or biologically based causes. It relies heavily upon neo-Darwinistic concepts and uses two basic premises derived from synthetic theory: (1) macroevolution, and (2) the "selfishness" of the gene.

Macroevolution (also known as "punctuated equilibria," or "punctuationism") refers to the importance of considering major, more abrupt evolutionary changes at the larger population levels (as opposed to *microevolution*, or "gradualism," which pertains to smaller, more gradual changes over time). The "selfishness" of the gene implies that the ultimate purpose of life is to preserve the genes and to pass them on to offspring. This is classical Darwinism made radical, where survival of the gene (as opposed to survival of the individual) is deemed paramount. In Wilson's words: "In a Darwinist sense the organism does not live for itself. Its primary function is not even to produce other organisms; it reproduces genes, and it serves as their temporary carrier."[11] This same idea became the basis for an entire book by Richard Dawkins titled *The Selfish Gene*. His thesis, quite simply, is that "we are survival machines—robot vehicles blindly programmed to preserve the selfish molecules known as genes."[12]

The epitome of avant-garde Darwinism can be found in a recent article titled "Is a New and General Theory of Evolution Emerging?" by Stephen Jay Gould.[13] Gould, a professor at Harvard University, is one of the leading spokesmen in the ultra-Darwinist movement.

Although he refers in his paper to the emergence of a "new theory," he is actually proposing the next step in Darwinian revisionism after the synthetic theory. Claiming that synthetic theory is too reductionistic—that is, it endeavors to reduce all evolutionary phenomena to nothing but discrete physicochemical processes—his alternative (although he proposes no new theory—just intimations) is to move away from concepts associated with microevolution. He would also like to replace reductionism with a hierarchical model of the world, a series of interconnected and semiindependent levels representing organismic progression and complexity.[14] He further advocates that the new theory (whatever form it will take) "will restore to biology a concept of organism." Here, he is implying that in neo-Darwinism the organism has been mistakenly conceptualized as a "sphere"—as something prey to the forces of the environment and selection with little to contribute to its own evolutionary development.

For details on Gould's view that a new unified theory is emerging, the reader may consult the article. As mentioned, Gould is not providing this new theory; he only suggests certain trends it must consider. Regardless, it is significant to note that Gould, while recognizing future trends in evolutionary theory, never in fact leaves the Darwinist camp; he never questions the key assumptions upon which neo-Darwinian theory is grounded.

Although not cited by Gould, a unified theory along lines he intimates is already available and in print. This is the theory of Erich Jantsch, as delineated in his two books *Design for Evolution* (1975) and

The Self-Organizing Universe (1980). Jantsch relies heavily upon the research findings of Ilya Prigogine, the Belgian physical chemist and winner of the 1977 Nobel Prize in chemistry. Although Prigogine's findings are quite technical, the basic principle and implications of his "theory of dissipative structures" can be well understood by nonscientists.

Briefly, the theory states that the structures of all living (and some nonliving) systems are perpetuated by the continual exchange of energy-flow between themselves and their environment. These dissipative structures take in particular forms of energy and process and release it in altered forms. The more complex in design a structure is, the more energy it consumes and processes. However, at any given time such an "open" system may take in more energy than it is capable of processing. Then it is forced to reorganize and refine its dynamics and structure into a greater complexity, which then increases its tendency for yet more energy consumption and consequent destabilization, this time to a higher degree. The cycle thus accelerates, the organism ever refining its internal energy systems and reintegrating itself into the general environment via its expanding connections to surrounding systems.

It should be noted that in the context of the foregoing processes, the idea of destabilization is synonymous with, or at least requisite to, flexibility. Any system that is inflexible is closed and devolving. This fact holds for any physical system, including the universe itself. Here is where Prigogine's theory begins to have ramifications far beyond earthly biophysics, for its logic of syntropy, as opposed to entropy, posits an unfinalized fate for the known cosmos, which runs counter to the Second Law of Thermodynamics. Although the First Law states that matter is neither created nor destroyed, the Second Law states that its change is only from a relatively ordered state to a disordered one, from organization to random chaos. Moreover, this Entropy Law says that any energy expended in the temporary creation of order simply accelerates the entropy process. "Time's arrow" is thereby sped in only one direction: to the ultimate heat-death of the observable universe.

The Laws of Thermodynamics are cornerstones of classical physics that remain empirically in place today. However, the development of the theory of relativity and of quantum physics has ushered in new hypotheses of the cosmos based on overwhelming evidence that these laws, basic as they may appear to be, must nonetheless alter or break down where (and when) the physics gets unusual. Whether the cosmos is infinitely pulsating in cycles of expansion and contraction, whether it is spherical, saddle-shaped, or ultimately shapeless, one thing is certain: it is essentially dynamic, and any law or set of laws we are able to formulate about it in our local neighborhood cannot be extrapolated across the board to the whole. The terms "open" and "closed" even cease to have much meaning on the cosmic scale. But on the scale of organismic existence the theory of dissipative structures further advances our understanding of the importance of syntropy and its heretofore unsuspected role in the evolutionary process.

In his two books, Jantsch not only utilizes Prigogine's findings and theories, but in eclectic fashion draws upon numerous lines of diverse research and progressive scientific thinking to substantiate his "unified" theory. The theory is too intricate and expansive to review here. Suffice it to say, it is not a complete break from Darwinism (as Darwin's views are encompassed) and does not adequately spell out *how* evolution takes place and *why* it takes place and, most importantly, fails to explain *which* organismic mechanisms allow evolutionary transmutation to occur at all. His "systems theory" is so eclectic and ambitious that it fails to be specific enough to provide us with adequate, concrete guidelines. (For example, in *The Self-Organizing Universe*, Jantsch provides several diagrams, one summarizing his evolutionary position in one grand sweep; it includes everything from "spatial structuration" to "epigenetic freedom" to "energy penetration" ... *mutates mutandi* ... implying literally hundreds of different key operations or processes, simultaneously interactive at twenty to thirty different levels of analysis or multiple dimensionality.)[15]

As you can surmise, almost nothing is left out. Jantsch's theory is just too encyclopedic. Perhaps Jantsch and Gould might collaborate, since they have essentially the same thing in mind; and possibly Gould's mental discipline would meld with Jantsch's inventiveness. Jantsch's books also provide no acknowledgment of the views of Lamarck, who proposed the first true transformational theory of evolution, even though the Jantsch adaptation of Progogine's ideas is presumably a theory of evolutionary transformation.

To summarize, Darwinism has passed through four main stages of revisionism over the past 120 years. The present stage, ultra-Darwinism, is merely a sophisticated complex resulting from the many years of revisionism, still tied to the basic assumptions of a classical Darwinism and neo-Darwinism (by our earlier analogy, digging the same hole deeper and deeper). More recent efforts to escape the weaknesses of Darwinian dogma include those of Prigogine and Jantsch; however, these appear to be too vague or all-embracing, while failing to confront many key issues of concern to scientific evolutionists.

Chapter Seven

PARADIGM
LOST

Evolutionism, purporting to explain all and everything solely and exclusively by natural selection for adaptation and survival, is the most extreme product of the materialistic utilitarianism of the nineteenth-century. The inability of twentieth-century thought to rid itself of this imposture is a failure which may well cause the collapse of Western civilization.

E. F. Schumacher,
A Guide for the Perplexed

It has been pointed out more than once by thinkers and wise men that man (even scholars and scientists) will often close his hand upon air, thinking all the while that he is holding some priceless gem, such as a bright, shiny emerald.

If not an emerald, then the flailing man is often clutching at straws. The Darwinian theory itself is, basically, a house built of straw—something that's interesting to look at and seemingly viable, but come a strong wind ... The Darwinian theories that impress so many in academia are, under close scrutiny, seen to be heavily flawed or, as in several cases, polished imitations of real theory. The polishing continues with the so-called modern synthesis. But why, it might be asked, have these defective theories been so highly praised and widely accepted by scientists who should, and could, know better? The reasons are myriad.

As mentioned earlier, the impact of Darwin's research substantiating the *process* of evolution automatically carried with it an eventual acceptance of his *explanation* of evolution; additionally, there occurred a materialistic, positivistic *Zeitgeist* brewing within scientific circles in the late 19th and early 20th centuries with which the Darwinian random/mechanical system was in concordance. There was also, in the West at least, a movement toward industrialism, capitalism, and super-independence that fostered a belief in "Social Darwinism," or the survival of the fittest within human society. And especially into the 20th century, an antireligious, atheistic, and agnostic backlash accompanied an increase in mass public education—and a questioning attitude in people in general—and this, too, enhanced the acceptance of Darwinism. Darwinism became an unconscious religious replacement for conventional religion. For many, *The Origin of Species* became the new bible.

For these and other reasons, any flaws in Darwinian systems were largely ignored and criticisms were rejected outright. "Group think" prevailed.

Columbia University professor Robert Nisbet is an astute scholar who has recognized the declining sanctity of "the once-sovereign Darwinian writ" among younger scientists. Referring to the Darwinist establishment as a "mandarinate," he asserts that the myth that Darwinism is synonymous with evolutionism is inevitably being laid to rest, along with the notion that anti-Darwinism must always be the uncerebral utterances of creationists.[1]

The major difficulty with Darwinism is that it is overly reductionistic, materialistic, and mechanistic. In this regard it emulates physics by attempting to reduce biological phenomena to elementary bits and pieces. Many biologists today do not consider a biological phenomenon real unless it is reducible to an explanation from physics.

Thus everything in the living world is reduced to machinery—all living organisms are "nothing but" passive automata manipulated by the environment. For Darwinians, evolution is the result of nothing but random mutations and fortuitous selection.

Reductionism and mechanistics are problematic for Darwinism, because many biological phenomena are, quite simply, not reducible to their component parts. There are multitudes of cases in the living world of what is now described as *synergy*; an example is water, a substance which transcends its mere components of two parts hydrogen and one part oxygen. Reductionism also discards one of the most fundamental qualities of life—consciousness (including experience, feeling, mind, etc.). Yet, it is generally agreed in more enlightened circles that, in higher forms of life at least, intellect, awareness, and consciousness have evolved at least parallel to body and form.

Further, reductionism based upon the mechanistic model of physics has actually been rejected by the physicists themselves. Modern, advanced physics has undergone an antimechanistic revolution, revealing the ultimate "components" of physical reality to be not small bits and pieces but variants of energy and dynamic events.[2] So, while Darwinian-based biology strives so diligently to emulate physics, physics itself is headed in a very different, more vitalistic and multidimensional direction.

More contemporary thinking in physics, psychology, and progressive biological circles has it that a comprehensive (or holistic) perspective must be adopted in place of mere mechanistic reductionism. Following the lead of a non-Darwinian, biologist Ludwig von Bertalanffy, these progressives are beginning to conceptualize living organisms and phenomena in terms of systems. Bertalanffy tagged this approach General Systems Theory (GST), which views organisms and their internal/external ecosystems as hierarchies of interdependent, dynamic organizational structures and forces. In Bertalanffy's view, the basic issue of evolution is not just the origin of species, but the "origin of organization"—understanding the organizational principles that underlie, and assist, the development of new species.

As a result of the holistic/systems movement and the broadened, more sophisticated perspective it encourages, the Darwinian assumptions of randomness, accident, fortuity, and so forth—the grand interplay of blind forces—are being confronted as insufficient, if not meaningless. In their place is a return to such metaconcepts as design, order, purpose, direction, values, and meaning. (The holistic/systems' perspective does not, however, totally exclude randomness and/or accident from within its sphere, only pointing out that random events and the like occur against a background of more fundamental and enduring principles and patterns.)

In this light, writer Colin Wilson, referring to Darwinism, pulls no philosophical punches, stating that any system of science, belief, or knowledge that excludes purpose or will is "an obstruction to human evolution ... a dangerous nuisance."[3]

The flaws in Darwinian theories, especially neo-Darwinian, are legion, but they can be grouped into various types: logical fallacies, tautological errors (i.e., circular thinking), mathematical improbabilities, lack of evidence, and inadequacies in accounting for human evolution. These problem areas are further elaborated upon here.

LOGIC

Before continuing, consider this simple cartoon by Ashleigh Brilliant.[4]

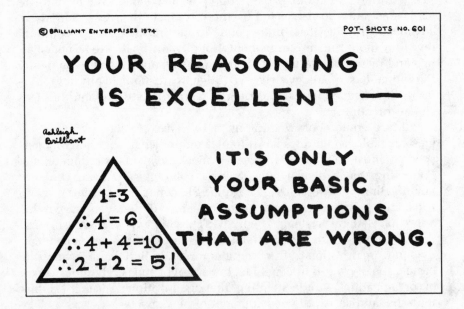

The biggest problem with Darwinian theory is actually very simple: its assumptions and premises are questionable. But people tend to ignore their assumptions, and this is probably why those of Darwinian theory have rarely been challenged. To review, there are three main premises in Darwinism:

1. *Mutations* are responsible for the transformation of species.

2. *Natural selection*—or the "weeding out" principle of the "survival of the fittest"—acts upon mutations (adaptive or deleterious) to favor certain members of the species over others.

3. Both of the above are *random* processes. In other words, mutations are accidental, and natural selection is fortuitous or due to chance.

These three premises are the bulwark of modern Darwinian theory. Yet, not only are they questionable, but almost all the evidence available contradicts their acceptance. Although the evidence will be considered later on in this chapter, some of the more obvious contradictions include the following:

Mutations are typically harmful or lethal (an "adaptive" mutation has never been produced in the laboratory).

Natural selection can only allow for the *strengthening* of a trait or characteristic (behavioral, physiological, anatomical) that is *already* present—it produces nothing new.

Both ideas—mutation and natural selection—are used *tautologically* or in *a posteriori* fashion (invoked after the fact).

The mathematical likelihood of producing evolutionary results from random, accidental processes is minuscule.

So, if the basic Darwinian assumptions are questionable to begin with, how can the theory itself be considered valid? It really can't be. But as Brilliant's cartoon illustrates, the curious fact about theories is that once you accept their assumptions, and their corollaries and deductions are derived according to correct logic, the theory may *seem* to be correct. Darwinian theory's logical coherence and, in the case of synthetic theory, eloquence, tend to override its reality whether it accounts for the evidence or not; the theory hypnotizes us, much like a grand obsession.

Thus, Darwinian theory in its synthetic form may be logically coherent, but if its premises are false, or even questionable, then the theory itself can be considered false or questionable. Logical coherence is easy to attain and is a minor achievement. The question remains: is the synthetic theory a theory of evolution? Does it explain whatever it claims to explain? Alas, it does not. Its overriding flaw is that it isn't a theory of evolution at all. It is actually only a theory about survival, adaptation, reproductivity, population genetics, and population demographics. It is a logically coherent system, based upon questionable (or false) assumptions, which is misplaced. That is, it claims to be explaining something that it does not really explain and is actually explaining something else—albeit something of related interest.

The analogy is with a game. All games are built upon certain assumptions or rules. An example is the game of football. Once you accept the rules, and play by the rules, the game makes sense—it's logically coherent. And with the basic rules at the foundation, many "corollaries" or permutations are made possible. In football, numerous formations and thousands of plays are possible. These many possibilities have even been submitted to statistical analysis and can be programmed into computers (one application is in the computerized electronic games so popular these days). Very impressive—and even eloquent. But a problem would arise if football players and fans suddenly began to believe that the game of football was applicable to everyday life—to understanding human behavior, social behavior, the movement of the planets, the purpose of life and the universe, and even *evolution*. Granted, the game of football and how it is played may tell us *something* about everyday life—such as about competition, survival, strategy, bravery. But we would be utterly mistaken if we considered that the game and its rules told us about things for which it really is not qualified.

The analogy relates well to the Darwinian theory of evolution. The synthetic theory, with all its corollaries, statistics, and technical terminology, although impressive and persuasive, is actually not that much further advanced than a sophisticated game of football, chess, or bridge, and all their fancy formations and permutations.

TAUTOLOGY

A tautology is a circular argument, or the substituting of one word-label for another. Merely verbal duplication, it rarely tells us anything significant about reality. But like logically coherent theories, the tautology can often hold a spell over our minds.

Tautologies come in different but related forms. One example is: "It will either rain or not rain today." This is a true statement, but what does it tell us? In actuality it tells us virtually nothing; we would know just as much about our day if the statement had never been uttered. Another example is: "Sleeping pills have soporific qualities." Again, true. But did you know that *soporific* means the "ability to produce sleep"? This is circularity, the juggling of words to produce a seemingly significant but trivial statement.

In synthetic theory, *mutation* and *selection* are often used tautologically. We see pseudoexplanatory statements like, "The evolution of this species is the result of mutations combined with selection." Yet evolution is synonymous with mutation/selection. The pseudoexplanation is especially common when selection is discussed: "Selection is based on the principle of 'survival of the fittest.'" "That which survives is 'fit' and that which is 'fit' survives." With the newer Darwinian theories, such as Kimura's Neutral Theory (see chapter 6, pp. 41–42), the tautologies persist: evolution is seen as largely due to genetic drift instead of to selection, while genetic drift is defined as "evolution (or change in gene frequencies)." The gist of all this is that *evolution equals genetic drift equals change in gene frequencies*: a three-way play on words.

Related to tautologies is the phenomenon of *a posteriori* inference, or after-the-fact labeling. Again, pseudoexplanation. No one has ever observed the evolution of a new species, especially not occurring by way of selection combined with accidental genetic mutation. Adaptive genetic mutation or natural selection is brought in after the fact—there is no independent criterion to define either of these processes or principles. There is no way, in advance, to independently determine if a mutation will be viable and/or if it will be selected out for possible evolutionary change. This very fundamental problem, amplified upon by the well-known philosopher Karl Popper, is known as the *principle of falsification*. Because the key concepts in Darwinian theory are tautologically defined and related, and since there is no independent definition of these concepts—which means they must be invoked after the fact (i.e., after evolution has already occurred)—then in this sense Darwinian theory as a whole is unfalsifiable. According to Popper, then, Darwinian theory is more a play on words than it is a scientific theory, since in principle truly scientific theories are potentially falsifiable.

Admittedly, this *a posteriori* problem probably cannot be totally eliminated. This is due to the nature of the evolutionary process itself, which has already happened and has occurred over a very long span of time. In addition, even though evolution is an ongoing process, it happens so slowly that it is difficult to "observe" in motion. But this does not completely excuse Darwinians from (1) not recognizing the tautological problem (which they rarely do), and (2) not keeping the problem under control (which they never do).

In this regard, Darwinians often rely upon a pseudoscientific ploy known as "proof by selected instances." The classic example, found in practically all introductory textbooks on biology, is that of *Biston betularia*, the peppered moth. Observations in northern Britain since the mid-1800s have revealed that the ratio of dark-colored to light-colored moths has increased considerably, as has the amount of pollution in nearby areas. The reason for the near-extinction of the light-colored moths is that pollution had darkened the trees where these moths alight, enabling the dark-colored moths to be camouflaged from the view of moth-eating birds. (Recently, however, due largely to the Clean Air Acts, the trees are becoming lighter in color, and now the ratio of light- to dark-colored moths is returning to normal.) This example is used not only as an illustration of natural selection in action, but also as proof of evolution and, further still, as proof of the Darwinian theory of evolution itself. The fallacy here is that, while this can be construed as an example of selection in nature, it in no way implies evolution, and certainly not Darwinian theory. If anything, the example illustrates how fortuity may in isolated instances affect survival. But neither survival *and* evolution, nor survival *and* Darwinian theory can be construed as synonymous. Although in this example one feature of the moth (dark color) is favored over another (light color), this is not evolution *per se*, since evolution entails formation of a *new* species. In the moth example, a new species of insect is not being developed, only the mere preservation of an existent one.

The theoretical problems that befall the Darwinian system are reminiscent of those that have also affected Freudian psychoanalysis (and encouraged its subsequent decline). Besides being founded upon questionable assumptions, the theoretical eloquence of Freudian theory itself has made its range too broad, allowing it to account for virtually anything; it has been stretched and interpreted to explain almost anything it desires according to its particular bent or motive (the ultimate motive being "to be right"). This conceptual "sleight-of-hand," as Theodore Roszak dubs it, appears convincing up to a point, based as it is on the dexterous shufflings of selective logic and research. But then its players overextend their game. Darwinists now hold, for instance, that random mutation even includes chemical, prebiotic evolution. But why should chemical evolution repeatedly, without fail, roll the way of biological life as we have it, when this is only one remote possibility out of an infinite spectrum? This is a gap of logic requiring faith or incredulity to fall into. Evolutionary probabilities have here become a very long dice game in which the neo-Darwinists ask us to believe that nothing but snake-eyes have come up. Remember, the Darwinists are talking about *pure chance* on every "roll" of mutation. Further, as Roszak notes, the extension of the key Darwinian concepts of natural selection and adaptation to the realm of chemicals makes no sense whatsoever, "since nonvital chemicals have before them no necessary task of surviving and reproducing, and so are exempt from extinction in any biological sense of the word."[5]

MATHEMATICAL IMPROBABILITIES

As evolutionary theory went the way of mathematical probability in physics, the random-mutation argument entered a statistical no-man's land. Few of Darwin's nonmathematical opponents cared or dared to enter the twilight realm of randomness. But those who were competent to take on the numbers game demonstrated that it took no genius to prove the improbability of chance mutation as the prime factor in evolution. In fact, once the digits are brought into line with actual prebiotic, molecular, and organic developments, life looks so infinitely rarefied in design as to be rightly called preprogrammed and, dare we say, purposeful?

The question is quite direct: What is the statistical probability that the evolution and development of all life as we know it on earth can be due to *random* forces (and in combination with accidental mutations and natural, undirected selection)?

The answer, which has been arrived at by astute mathematicians and scientists, is that it is not only improbable but *highly unlikely*.

A number of investigators have looked at the likelihood of random mutations effecting new structures, such as those we see in life forms, at all levels. These thinkers and researchers, many of them with excellent mathematical backgrounds, have shown quite clearly that the random mutational process cannot account for the immense amount of ordered informational content and systematization involved in the development and composition of structures (at all levels) making up life forms.

One scientist, J. R. Pratt, made comparisons between something familiar, the information content of instruction books, and the information in genetic DNA chains. For example, a mere virus with one DNA chain, say 200,000 bases long, has 60,000 words in its "instructional book," a book that would contain at least 30 pages written in English. The instruction book for a bacterium, however, would be 10 to 100 times larger than this. Pratt concludes that a human would require a 46-volume, million-page encyclopedia to equal its genetic information, with about 20,000 words per volume (this based on *one* somatic cell with its 46 chromosomes).[6] W. H. Thorpe, in commenting upon Pratt's observations, adds that these staggering genetic numbers do not "specify the detailed positions, actions and functions of the great hordes of molecules in each cell."[7]

If, as Thorpe suggests, we merely consider one tenth of the gene supply in a human, there are still 10^8 bits of information (100 volumes of our encyclopedia). The main question is—can the idea of a random mutational process account for this great degree of order? Not really. The idea of the complex uniqueness of the gene is directly incompatible with the concept of random mutation (and random selection).

Others have come to the same conclusion. F. B. Salisbury, working independently of Pratt, arrived at similar computations. He concluded that DNA in humans contains 10^9 nucleotide pairs per nucleus, and in other organisms 10^7 to 10^{11}. Using our instructional-book analogy, to replicate this information in English would take about a thousand volumes (10^9 bits per page and 500 pages per volume).[8]

mRNA START →   A START

CCGTCAGGATTGACACCCTCCCAATTGTATGTTTTCATGCCTCCAAATCTT**GGAGG**CTTTTT**ATGG**TTCGTTCTTATTACCCTTCTGAA

TGTCACGCTGATTATTTTGACTTTGAGCGTATCGAGGCTCTTAAACCTGCTATTGAGGCTTGTGGCATTTCTACTCTTTCTCAATCCCCA

ATGCTTGGCTTCCATAAGCAGATGGATAACCGCATCAAGCTCTTGGAAGAGATTCTGTCTTTTCGTATGCAGGGCGTTGAGTTCGATAAT

GGTGATATGTATGTTGACGGCCATAAGGCTGCTTCTGACGTTCGTGATGAGTTTGTATCTGTT**ACT**GAGAAGTTAATGGATGAATTGGCA

CAATGCTACAATGTGCTCCCCCAACTTGATATTAATAACACTATAGACCACCGCCCCGAAGGGGACGAAAAATGGTTTTTAGAGAACGAG
|— REGION OF ORIGIN OF DNA REPLICATION —|

AAGACGGTTACGCAGTTTTGCCGCAAGCTGGCTGCTGAACGCCCTCTTAAGGATATTCGCGATGAGTATAATTACCCCAAAAAGAAAGGT

ATTAAGGATGAGTGTTCAAGATTGCTGGAGGCCTCCACTAAGTATCGCGTAGAGGCTTTGCTATTCAGCGTTTGATGAATGCAATGCGA

CAGGCTCATGCTGATGGTTGGTTTATCGTTTTTGACACTCTCACGTTGGCTGACGACCGATTAGAGGCGTTTTATGATAATCCCAATGCT

TTGCGTGACTATTTTCGTGATATTGGTCGTATGGTTCTTGCTGCCGAGGGTCGCAAGGCTAATGATTCACACGCCGACTGCTATCAGTAT

TTTTGTGTGCCTGAGTATGGTACAGCTAATGGCCGTCTTCATTTCCATGCGGTGCACTTTATGCGGACACTTCCTACAGGTAGCGTTGAC
mRNA START →

CCTAATTTTGGTCGTCGGATACGCAATCGCCGCCAGTTAAATAGCTTGCAAAATACGTGGCCTTATGGTTACAGTATGCCCATCGCAGTT

CGCTACACGCAGGACGCTTTTTCACGTTCTGGTTGGTTGTGGCCTGTTGATGCTAAAGGTGAGCCGCTTAAAGCTACCAGTTATATGGCT
                                                                              B START

GTTGGTTTCTATGTGGCTAAATACGTTAACAAAAAGTCAGATATGGACCTTGCTGCTAAAGGTCT**AGGAG**CTAAAGA**ATGG**AACAACTCA

CTAAAAACCAAGCTGTCGCTACTTCCCAAGAAGCTGTTCAGAATCAGAATGAGCCGCAACTTCGGGATGAAAATGCTCACAATGACAAAT

CTGTCCACGGAGTGCTTAATCCAACTTACCAAGCTGGGTTACGACGCGACGCCGTTCAACCAGATATTGAAGCAGAACGCAAAAAGAGAG

ATGAGATTGAGGCTGGGAAAAGTTACTGTAGCCGACGTTTTGGCGGCGCAACCTGTGACGACAAATCTGCTCAAATTTATGCGCGCTTCG
                                                                        B END

ATAAAAATGATTGGCGTATCCAACCTGCAGAGTTTTATCGCTTCCATGACGCAGAAGTTAACACTTTCGGATATTTC**TGA**TGAGTCGAAA
                                                                C START   A END

AATTATCTTGATAAAGCAGGAATTACTACTGCTTGTTTACGAATTAAATCGAAGTGGACTGCTGGCGGAAA**ATGA**GAAAATTCGACCTAT

CCTTGCGCAGCTCGAGAAGCTCTTACTTTGCGACCTTTCGCCATCAACTAACGATTCTGTCAAAAACTGACGCGTTGGATGAGGAGAAGT

GGCTTAATATGCTTGGCACGTTCGTCAAGGACTGGTTTAGATATGAGTCACATTTTGTTCATGGTAGAGATTCTCTTGTTGACATTTTAA
mRNA START →   D START   C END

AAGAGCGTGGATTACTATCTGAGTCCGATGCTGTTCAACCACTAATA**GGT**AAGAAATC**ATGA**GTCAAGTTACTGAACAATCCGTACGTTT

CCAGACCGCTTTGGCCTCTATTAAGCTCATTCAGGCTTCTGCCGTTTTGGATTTAACCGAAGATGATTTCGATTTTCTGACGAGTAACAA
                                       E START

AGTTTGGATTGCTACTGACCGCTCTCGTGCTCGTCGCTGCGTT**GAGG**CTTGCGTTT**ATGG**TACGCTGGACTTTGTAGGATACCCTCGCTT

TCCTGCTCCTGTTGAGTTTATTGCTGCCGTCATTGCTTATTATGTTCATCCCGTCAACATTCAAACGGCCTGTCTCATCATGGAAGGCGC

TGAATTTACGGAAAACATTATTAATGGCGTCGAGCGTCCGGTTAAAGCCGCTGAATTGTTCGCGTTTACCTTGCGTGTACGCGCAGGAAA
                                                       E END D END J START

CACTGACGTTCTTACTGACGCAGAAGAAAACGTGCGTCAAAAATTACGTGCGG**AAGGAG**T**GA**TG**TAA**T**G**TCTAAAGGTAAAAAACGTTCT
J END   F START

TAATTGCAGGGGCTTCGGCCCCTTACTTG**AGGA**TAAATT**ATG**TCTAATATTCAAACTGGCGCCGAGCGTATGCCGCATGACCTTTCCCAT

CTTGGCTTCCTTGCTGGTCAGATTGGTCGTCTTATTACCATTTCAACTACTCCGGTTATCGCTGGCGACTCCTTCGAGATGGACGCCGTT

GGCGCTCTCCGTCTTTCTCCATTGCGTCGTGGCCTTGCTATTGACTCTACTGTAGACATTTTTACTTTTTATGTCCCTCATCGTCACGTT

```
TATGGTGAACAGTGGATTAAGTTCATGAAGGATGGTGTTAATGCCACTCCTCTCCCGACTGTTAACACTACTGGTTATATTGACCATGCC

GCTTTTCTTGGCACGATTAACCCTGATACCAATAAAATCCCTAAGCATTTGTTTCAGGGTTATTTGAATATCTATAACAACTATTTTAAA

GCGCCGTGGATGCCTGACCGTACCGAGGCTAACCCTAATGAGCTTAATCAAGATGATGCTCGTTATGGTTTCCGTTGCTGCCATCTCAAA

AACATTTGGACTGCTCCGCTTCCTCCTGAGACTGAGCTTTCTCGCCAAATGACGACTTCTACCACATCTATTGACATTATGGGTCTGCAA

GCTGCTTATGCTAATTTGCATACTGACCAAGAACGTGATTACTTCATGCAGCGTTACCATGATGTTATTTCTTCATTTGGAGGTAAAACC

TCATATGACGCTGACAACCGTCCTTTACTTGTCATGCGCTCTAATCTCTGGGCATCTGGCTATGATGTTGATGGAACTGACCAAACGTCG

TTAGGCCAGTTTTCTGGTCGTGTTCAACAGACCTATAAACATTCTGTGCCGCGTTTCTTTGTTCCTGAGCATGGCACTATGTTTACTCTT

GCGCTTGTTCGTTTTCCGCCTACTGCGACTAAAGAGATTCAGTACCTTAACGCTAAAGGTGCTTTGACTTATACCGATATTGCTGGCGAC

CCTGTTTTGTATGGCAACTTGCCGCCGCGTGAAATTTCTATGAAGGATGTTTTCCGTTCTGGTGATTCGTCTAAGAAGTTTAAGATTGCT

GAGGGTCAGTGGTATCGTTATGCGCCTTCGTATGTTTCTCCTGCTTATCACCTTCTTGAAGGCTTCCCATTCATTCAGGAACCGCCTTCT

GGTGATTTGCAAGAACGCGTACTTATTCGCAACCATGATTATGACCAGTGTTTCAGTCGTTCAGTTGTTGCAGTGGATAGTCTTACCTCA

                                                       F END
TGTGACGTTTATCGCAATCTGCCGACCACTCGCGATTCAATCATGACTTCGTGA‾TAAAAGATTGAGTGTGAGGTTATAACCGAAGCGGTA
                                                                                  G START
AAAATTTTAATTTTTGCCGCTGAGGGGTTGACCAAGCGAAGCGCGGTAGGTTTTCTGCTTAGGAGTTTAATCATGTTTCAGACTTTTATT
                                                                         │···│
TCTCGCCACAATTCAAACTTTTTTTCTGATAAGCTGGTTCTCACTTCTGTTACTCCAGCTTCTTCGGCACCTGTTTTACAGACACCTAAA

GCTACATCGTCAACGTTATATTTTGATAGTTTGACGGTTAATGCTGGTAATGGTGGTTTTCTTCATTGCATTCAGATGGATACATCTGTC

AACGCCGCTAATCAGGTTGTTTCAGTTGGTGCTGATATTGCTTTTGATGCCGACCCTAAATTTTTTTGCCTGTTTGGTTCGCTTTGAGTCT

TCTTCGGTTCCGACTACCCTCCCGACTGCCTATGATGTTTATCCTTTGGATGGTCGCCATGATGGTGGTTATTATACCGTCAAGGACTGT

GTGACTATTGACGTCCTTCCCCGTACGCCCGGCAATAACGTCTACGTTGGTTTCATGGTTTGGTCTAACTTTACCGCTACTAAATGCCGC
                                                           G END      H START
GGATTGGTTCGCTGAATCAGGTTATTAAAGAGATTATTTGTCTCCAGCCACTTAAGTGA‾GGTGATTTATG‾TTTGGTGCTATTGCTGGCG
                                                              │···│
GTATTGCTTCTGCTCTTGCTGGTGGCGCCATGTCTAAATTGTTTGGAGGCGGTCAAAAAGCCGCCTCCGGTGGCATTCAAGGTGATGTGC

TTGCTACCGATAACAATACTGTAGGCATGGGTGATGCTGGTATTAAATCTGCCATTCAAGGCTCTAATGTTCCTAACCCTGATGAGGCCG

CCCCTAGTTTTGTTTCTGGTGCTATGGCTAAAGCTGGTAAAGGACTTCTTGAAGGTACGTTGCAGGCTGGCACTTCTGCCGTTTCTGATA

AGTTGCTTGATTTGGTTGGACTTGGTGGCAAGTCTGCCGCTGATAAAGGAAAGGATACTCGTGATTATCTTGCTGCTGCATTTCCTGAGC

TTAATGCTTGGGAGCGTGCTGGTGCTGATGCTTCCTCTGCTGGTATGGTTGACGCCGGATTTGAGAATCAAAAAGAGCTTACTAAAATGC

AACTGGACAATCAGAAAGAGATTGCCGAGATGCAAAATGAGACTCAAAAAGAGATTGCTGGCATTCAGTCGGCGACTTCACGCCAGAATA

CGAAAGACCAGGTATATGCACAAAATGAGATGCTTGCTTATCAACAGAAGGAGTCTACTGCTCGCGTTGCGTCTATTATGGAAAACACCA

ATCTTTCCAAGCAACAGCAGGTTTCCGAGATTATGCGCCAAATGCTTACTCAAGCTCAAACGGCTGGTCAGTATTTTACCAATGACCAAA

TCAAAGAAATGACTCGCAAGGTTAGTGCTGAGGTTGACTTAGTTCATCAGCAAACGCAGAATCAGCGGTATGGCTCTTCTCATATTGGCG
                                                                    H END
CTACTGCAAAGGATATTTCTAATGTCGTCACTGATGCTGCTTCTGGTGTGGTTGATATTTTT‾CATGGTATTGATAAAGCTGTTGCCGATA

CTTGGAACAATTTCTGGAAAGACGGTAAAGCTGATGGTATTGGCTCTAATTTGTCTAGGAAA‾TAA‾
```

begins with the noncoding region before the *A* gene and ends with the termination codon
of the *H* gene. The ribosome-recognition signals are shown in the shaded colored boxes,
the initiation codons in dotted boxes, and the termination codons in open black boxes.

Additionally, it has been found that some DNA sequences recur from a thousand to a million times per cell, hence a great deal is repetitive or redundant. When we consider that life is directly dependent upon this uniqueness and great degree of ordered informational content, this is more than can ever be handled by invoking the chance/mutational concept.

An illustration of the extreme difficulty facing Darwinists in attempting to account for the uniqueness and complexity of gene organization by way of random, accidental mutation and selection is brought out in a recent article, "The Nucleotide Sequence of a Viral DNA" by John C. Fiddes.[9] As the result of extensive investigation, Fiddes was able to determine the complete sequence of the 5375 nucleotides of the DNA (one strand) of the øχ174 virus. The complete sequence is provided in the accompanying figure.

The notion that accidental, random processes were responsible for this high degree of order and uniqueness is out of the question. And remember—the sequence shown in the illustration is for only *one single strand of viral DNA.*

An excellent source relating to the present issue is the book *Mathematical Challenges to the Neo-Darwinian Interpretation of Evolution,* in which several mathematical biologists take Darwinian theory to task. An article in the book by Marcel Schützenberger is unique. He carefully programmed a computer with the basic data derived from Darwinian theory in an attempt to show a resultant order resembling evolutionary development; the outcome was quite interesting—the machine repeatedly jammed. Schützenberger calculated that the mathematical probability of executing a successful program based on Darwinian principles was less than one divided by ten to the eleventh power.[10]

Another example that defies the Darwinian principle of evolution by random accumulation of favorable mutations is the formation of that complex structure the eye. Even Darwin found the eye baffling to his conceptions, calling the formation of this and other complex structures (such as the inner ear) the problem of "organs of extreme perfection." The human eye is dazzlingly complex; it includes in its intricate, delicate mechanisms the iris and cornea, the automatic lens, and its retina containing 130 million light-sensitive rods and cones. Then there is the eyelid, the eye muscles, and the optic nerve that connects to a specific area of the brain. All comprise one finely tuned, integrated system, each of its multimillion parts having had to evolve in *unison,* developmentally coordinated in time and space. Although, as mentioned, Darwin was quite astounded by this, he speculated that the eye might have come about by a series of happy accidents, provided it happened gradually, over long spans of time. But, as Darwin's critics have pointed out, this concept of *gradualism* leapfrogged over the initial question of how a primitive visual organ could have come about through random factors in the first place, not to mention what survival value such a functionally incomplete eye (as with a partially evolved wing) could have.[11]

To cast the homely analogy of dice again, a moment's run of such "luck" is unbelievable by anyone's standards; millions of years' worth makes the idea of one mode succeeding by chance only look rather like a craps addict's obsession with staying in the game after losing more than 99.99 percent of the time. Is he really in the game now, or is he dreaming he is? And since he has at least that much less percentage of his starting stakes, which must have been quite prodigious, we can say with some assurance that he is indeed dreaming.

In this connection, it is significant that Darwinists typically use the idea of vast time-spans as a means of explaining how order might result from randomness—long time-spans allowing for random processes to eventually arrange themselves toward direction and order. But, paradoxically, the notion of vast time-spans actually militates *against* the Darwinian view. This is due to the biological phenomenon of *equilibrium*, which in effect demonstrates that increasing the time factor in reversible reactions simply *increases* the likelihood that equilibrium will be achieved rather than the improbable. Improbable biological features wrought by mutations or random selection would, given enough time, be *eliminated* rather than perpetuated. Since evolution entails an increasing in complexity of life forms over time, and not simply equilibrium, then principles other than Darwinian ones are undoubtedly involved.[12]

On a more macroscopic level, other writers have drawn the same conclusions. Here we have the classic "teleology versus randomness" argument. *Teleology* implies the notion of purpose. Man, animals, plants, earth, the universe, and so on are viewed by the teleologists as highly intricate forms or systems, and also as great products of design. Since all created of design familiar to humankind are the deliberate result of purposive planning, it is concluded in this argument that humanity itself as well as other life forms must be the result of planned design and not random processes. In this connection, Roszak makes the case quite clear:

> On what then does selective pressure act..., unless upon some inadmissible tendency (intention) of atoms and molecules to create complex forms and hierarchical structure in the universe? But here again we are to believe that by pure chance the genetic chemistry of life has simply fallen into place—just as the collected works of Shakespeare would surely be produced by the proverbial roomful of monkeys banging on typewriters ... if given enough time.[13]

THE EVIDENCE (OR LACK OF IT)

A great deal of evidence is available that contradicts the Darwinian view, as well as evidence that it cannot explain. There are hundreds of studies and findings that apply; however, space permits citing only a few examples and stating the main arguments against Darwinism.

Genetic Mutations Are Typically Harmful and Lethal

As mentioned, mutations occur as the result of accidental events or agents, such as radiation, cosmic rays, undirected chemical or micromechanical shocks, microscopic lesions, and the like.

Few, if any, laboratory or naturally produced mutations have ever been shown to result in other than harm or death to the affected lifeform. Professor C. P. Martin of McGill University, an esteemed anatomist, has provided the most effective arguments on this point. Following a thorough review of the evidence, Martin concludes that mutations "do not supply the raw material" for selection. He emphasizes that mutations do overwhelmingly affect adversely the crucial trait of viability, and that the variations of viability are of "such supreme importance" that they would "take a higher priority over variations of any other characteristic."[14]

Theodosius Dobzhansky, a well-known genetic biologist who has been effecting genetic mutations in fruit flies for many years, has never been able to produce one viable mutation, let alone a new species or even a new adaptive strain. In his textbook *Evolution* he readily acknowledges, "Newly arisen mutations are more likely to be deleterious than beneficial to their carriers."[15] Yet, through painstaking experimentation, Dobzhansky has occasionally succeeded in producing a mutant strain such as a group with larger wings than normal, considering this a more "adaptive" strain. But this is begging the question. At least two problems arise with this interpretation—one admitted by Dobzhansky himself: (1) "This brings about the important point that mutations are not beneficial or harmful in the abstract, but rather with respect to some environment"[16]; and (2) while the mutant strains might have, say, larger wings, may not the mutation have some *deleterious* effect on some *other* part of the physiology/anatomy at the same time? If you are only looking at wing size, it is unlikely you would detect some other change as well, which might be harmful to the organism.

Basically, both of these points are related. The only "adaptive" characteristic of the mutant strain is in the mind of the (Darwinian) experimenter: in the abstract, removed from the natural environment or the niche of the fruit fly (or any other laboratory animal), there is no easy way to determine the significance of the mutation.

The Naiveté of Random Mutations When Considering Genotypic/Phenotypic Relationships

Genotype refers to the genetic constitution of an individual organism, designated with reference either to a single trait or a set of related traits. (*Genome* refers to the complete genetic constitution of the organism.) *Phenotype* refers to the observable (anatomical, physiological) properties of an organism, sometimes in reference to a specific trait or set of traits. (*Phenome* refers to the total, overt organism.)

There are two considerations that interest us here. First, every organism displays a natural rate of spontaneous mutations of genetic material in its lifetime. Some Darwinists have considered this significant. But spontaneous mutations must be shown to have the ability to facilitate more specific ("adaptive") mutations. Dobzhansky himself has admitted that evolutionary rates are probably not tied to mutational rates in any meaningful sense, since spontaneous mutations account for only "a small fraction of the genetic variation present in populations at any one time."[17]

Sexual recombination is now believed by Darwinists to be much more significant in determining genetic variation. Spontaneous rates of mutation are therefore not to be considered as necessarily contributing to evolution, unless as a backdrop or potential upon which macromutations might effect themselves.

Second, and more to the point, any major phenotypic trait or structure of any given species is usually under control of a *series* or *group* of genes, instead of one single gene. (There are a few exceptions: certain trivial features, like the color of the iris of the eye, or curly hair, or the rare recessive trait of hemophilia, etc., may depend on a single gene.) Therefore, if we are considering a phenotypic trait—what we normally do in discussing the evolution of a new species—we must realize that if that trait (e.g., the eye) is under control of several interrelated genes, then an "accidental mutation" affecting one gene, or even a few closely adjacent on a strand of chromosome, will not bring about the total required effect (e.g., the development of the eye). What is required is the *accidental simultaneous arrival* of many mutations at the exact loci of *all* the related genes in question. Again a highly unlikely affair. In order to get around this problem, some Darwinists have suggested that patterns of accidental mutations, or related groups of random mutations, be considered as explaining the phenotypic alterations in new species. But this implies a certain *directedness* and is self-contradictory vis-à-vis the randomness concept already inherent in the Darwinian position.

Arthur Koestler has made the same point in discussing a "holarchic" concept of the gene. Molecular biology, he reminds us, ushered in a boggling new complexity in genetic studies, and with it a likewise formidable terminology: repressor genes, corepressors, aporepressors, modifer genes, "operons," cistrons, and so on. These entities, along with genes that regulate the overall mutational rate, are in fact the components of what he coins a "genetic holarchy," a working, self-regulating agency of genetic control in the developing embryo "equipped with feedback devices from a hierarchy of environments which surround each and every cell."

The discovery of this intricate genetic organization renders unworkable the crude Darwinian model of chromosomal function as a neat linear unfolding, in the manner of a tape recorder. Koestler's holarchy would of necessity possess an essential stability and flexibility, enabling it not only to repair itself, but to protect the delicate embryo against its volatile environment and to safeguard the species against the random mutational dangers (phylogenetic) posed to its own chromosomal genes.

Koestler maintains that this "genetic microhierarchy" hypothesis has met considerable resistance among the synthetic theorists because "its acceptance would lead to a basic revaluation of our notions of the evolutionary process."[18]

Since most organisms possess a "genetic microhierarchy," this necessitates the operation of a pattern of mutations in order to produce the evolution of a new structure or species, something totally unlikely to occur by accident or chance. Something else—something non-Darwinian—is undoubtedly responsible.

Conflict with the Law of Parallel Embryological Development

The Law of Parallel Embryological Development embraces the common observation that evolution is recapitulated (or briefly restated) during embryological development and that the phenomenon occurs uniformly across all species. Hence, in the human, the developing embryo smoothly traverses its evolutionary history from single cell to fish to primate, and so forth, in its nine-month gestation journey.

Every laboratory study of the effect of accidental mutations upon embryological development has revealed that their induction occurs early on and that they carelessly "break in" on an established embryological sequence of unfoldment. Although mutations may not be visible until a succeeding stage, the evidence strongly indicates that all of them affect the embryo almost from the outset. This is supported by substantial research showing that mutations can be induced artificially only by introducing the inducing agent to the germ cells at an extremely early period.[19]

If this is the case, the idea that accidental mutations can be responsible (with the help of selection) for the development of new species' characteristics—that is, evolution—is untenable. This is so simply because, according to Darwinian theory, *new* traits (or mutations) would be expected to be introduced toward the *end* of the embryological sequence; this should also be expected to occur in a natural way, and instead would be highly disruptive.

Natural Selection and Competition Often Not Clearly Applicable

As you will recall, the idea of natural selection or survival of the fittest has been abused frequently enough, often assuming a tautological quality. In order to get around this, some writers have ventured to determine what it is that may independently define an adaptive trait or what may qualify as being of selective value. Darwinists complain that it is not possible to do this (like ostriches with their heads buried in the sand), since "selective value" is purely circumstantial. In other words—the tautology: Whatever traits the organism has already evolved are therefore of selective value.

But this is begging the question, and some astute scientists and writers have pointed out that certain traits and innate behaviors do *not* appear to be of selective value to the species in question. And since such traits/behaviors have persisted for millennia (or even millions of years) it is difficult to see how the *prima facie* idea of selective value can be as universal as the Darwinists claim—and more to the point, how it could play an integral role in evolution itself.

Yet the Darwinists have hinged their theories on only those cases that seem to support the selectionist principle, selectively ignoring those that don't. Consequently, by the 1920s most of the critics of the theory had simply given up trying to pin the issues down. But before then, ever since Darwin, a number of respected zoologists and alternative theorists had pointed out a diversity of particular animal traits that seemed to serve no selective function. Biologist Ludwig Von Bertalanffy has more recently brought some of these to attention. For example, no one has explained why the eels of Comacchio make their treacherous migrations to the Sargasso Sea. What survival advantage is there for an entire species to be programmed for this ritual peril? The same question applies to the four stomachs of the cow; why four when its fellow domestic vegetarian the horse, with a similar body and the same diet, gets along quite well with just one? And while numerous species have developed elaborate mimicries and camouflages for protection, why do so many others prosper in conspicuousness of shape and coloration?[20]

So "selective value" is a conceptual red herring indeed when held up only as evidence of competitive advantage due to accidental mutation. It is no redder than a certain strain of viceroy butterfly's imitation of its cousin, the monarch. The monarch produces in its body a chemical substance that causes convulsion and regurgitation in any bird hapless enough to eat one of these beautiful insects. Therefore most birds, by instinct or experience, avoid the monarch. The viceroy also profits from this wholesale aversion to its relative by having a close enough match of its wing pattern and color to turn away any bird the monarch does. But there is an interesting, perhaps telling, developmental difference. While the monarch's markings are incipient in its caterpillar stage, the viceroy's wait to appear—and then rather magically—on its adult wings following emergence from the chrysalis. This could suggest true mimicry in the viceroy, although there is no way of knowing that the monarch did indeed evolve and fly its colors first. Selectionist theory can tell us nothing either way, unless of course it is the butterfly's "selection"; but this intimates something far removed from Darwinism.

The implication is unavoidable: the notions of natural selection and selective value, at least as heretofore expounded, are misleading simplisms that hardly explain survival, much less evolution. No amount of Darwinian "probablies" or neo-Darwinian probabilities can enable them to.

C. P. Martin (*Psychology, Evolution and Sex*) also cites various cases in nature where the conventional notion of natural selection is clearly violated and cannot apply. For example, the caterpillar *Keliothis armigera* drills a hole in the fruit of the opium poppy for purposes of pupating, but in 70 to 90 percent of the cases the hole is too small for the developed moth to escape. For those caterpillars who drill large holes, the moth escapes, but for numerous millennia small-hole-drilling caterpillars have persisted, and their ensuing moths have died. Nonetheless, in spite of all the time natural selection (if valid) has had opportunity to work, it has not assisted in producing a race of caterpillars that always drill large holes. Obviously other factors must be operative, and natural selection cannot be as powerful and important a factor as the Darwinists like to believe.

Related to this is the idea of competition, which according to Darwinists plays an important role in evolution. Supposedly competition is encouraged in species with large populations; Darwinists believe this important in enhancing the operation of selection and, hence, increasing the probability of strengthening the species as a whole.

But in spite of the theory's insistence on these parameters in evolution, several writers have found this not to be the actual state of affairs in nature.

Martin has provided examples to show that, as a rule, population saturation typically leads to racial degeneration rather than to renewal and improvement. Crowded competition in fact appears as one of the prime conditions for deterioration among a great variety and number of plant and animal species. Too heavy seeding of agricultural crops and forests, in hope of higher yield, has consistently led to low production instead, a world-wide lesson painfully learned. Sunlight, air, and moisture are simply commodities that run out where space does.[21]

Among animals the effects of overpopulation are often socially lethal. Stress, pathological behavior, and physical disease rise inversely to the artificial diminishment of individual space, in both laboratory and natural habitat. In rat colonies sexual aberration and aggression increase dramatically and breeding decreases, resulting in the advancement of neither the majority nor a fit few, but in the decline of all.

Along these same lines Carl C. Lindegren, in his book *Cold War in Biology*, amplifies on the work of Fritz Wendt, Director of the Missouri Botanical Gardens, and Jens Clausen of Stanford University. Both these researchers, in working with plants and flowers, have shown quite clearly that in the natural propagation of flora, competition is the exception rather than the rule. Each plant seems to find a peculiar niche in the environment and fits that niche rather than competing with other organisms.[22]

As they regard fauna, the "struggle for existence" and competition for survival are also not so commonplace as generally implied by Darwinists. The cooperative and social characteristics (let alone the altruistic features) of animals must always be considered, and not simply as just another example of survivalist strategy. The intercooperative nature of many disparate species of animals and plants, living together, sharing the same environment, and not competitively, is surely more commonplace than the constant "struggle for survival" connected with Darwinian conceptions.

Recent research by John A. Wiens and John Rostenberry proves this out. These ornithologists studied several communities of breeding songbirds (eastern meadowlarks, dickcissels, grasshopper sparrows, western meadowlarks, horned larks, longspurs, sage thrashers, sage sparrows, and more) in the grasslands and shrubsteppe of western North America. According to Darwinian theory, Wiens and Rostenberry could initially "fully [expect] to find competition in these communities" (or even evidence of patterns suggesting competition in the past); but instead, they discovered the exact opposite to be true. Their conclusion: "We now think that direct, ongoing competition is infrequent in these systems and that it may have relatively little to do with the organization of bird communities."[23] (Asking himself why biologists since the time of Darwin have been so preoccupied with competition, Wiens comments, "Part of the answer is that we have used simplified theories." And further, "Our views have been influenced by their cultural context.... Competition also occupies a central position in Western culture.... After all, we have grown up immersed in such a world view.")[24]

As L. L. Whyte and Von Bertalanffy point out, the organizational upgrading that has led to the emergence of new and improved life forms appears to have taken place during the periods when the environmental niches were relatively vacant and competition at low ebb. This is panoramically evidenced in the invasion of land by the vertebrates, their backbones having already been developed in the sea. And having conquered the land, the vertebrates did not displace lower forms that served specific purposes in the ecology. Vis-à-vis each other, the mammals have not effaced the reptiles, nor the reptiles the amphibians, and so forth.[25]

The Domestication Argument as Faulty

In considering natural selection, it is interesting to note that, in principle, breeding involves purposeful "selecting out" under someone's direction, and that "directed selection" would be a more appropriate term than "natural selection," the term paradoxically chosen by Darwin—implying such "breeding" to be purely random and under no direction.

The well-known results of domestication and selective breeding influenced Darwin's thinking, and these were used to support his natural selection position. However, selection in nature has no parallel to selection in breeding. As Martin and others have shown, in reality many less suitable members, as well as those with nonadaptive features, continue to survive for long stretches of time, along with the more suitable features characteristic of the species.

Darwin's knowledge about domestication was lacking in other respects as well. Morphogenetic and behavioral changes in domesticated stock occur much too rapidly *en masse* for the snail's pace of natural selection. Gene theory being unknown to him, Darwin assumed that improvement of breeds was due to farmers' immediate weeding out of inferior individuals. But even at that time breeders had a fair inkling of the importance of good nutrition and shelter and were not quick to cast out weak and sick animals. Replacing them is not so fast and easy.

Also, Darwin was not agrarian enough to recognize that domesticated animals turn wild again in short order when released from their confines. The impact of supportive conditions on stock quality is now common knowledge; superior food and shelter produce superior strains, and this improvement accelerates (varying with different breeds) over generations when the conditions are maintained. Likewise, even the most superior stock will decline within several generations if the conditions are not kept up, regardless of ongoing selection policies.[26]

Evidence for the Inheritance of Acquired Characteristics

Certain lines of evidence, supporting the classical Lamarckian idea of the inheritance of acquired characteristics, are also challenging to the concept of random mutation. An example is the callosities on the knees of warthogs and ostriches, which are present at birth. Observations of these species indicate that they very frequently lower their knees to the ground for various purposes during their life, and the conclusion is that callosities have somehow been inherited as the result of prolonged use and exercise over many thousands of years. Other examples (found in various species, including humans) are the lines on our hands and the thickening of the soles of the feet, noticeable at birth.

Similarly, there is the fact of the inheritance of instincts. Certain instinctual behaviors are exhibited in many species directly following birth. (Examples are legion. Two of the more impressive are the food dance of the bee and the web of the spider. The "figure eight" wiggling dance of the worker bee communicates the location of a food source in a very precise and ingenious manner. Spiders can construct webs of a wide variety of shapes and sizes, many of which are extremely complex in design, suggesting a grasp of higher mathematical principles.) Since an instinct is itself a form of behavior, it would seem much more feasible that such instincts manifested as a result of repeated habits by the species over long stretches of time, rather than the mere manifestation of some fortuitous mutational effect.

The idea of repeated organ use (or disuse) over long stretches of time is central to Lamarckian and neo-Lamarckian explanations of evolution. August Weismann's attempt to discredit Lamarckians by repeatedly cutting off the tails of mice in order to produce a tailless variety (which of course failed) can be considered absurd in light of the use concept. Similar attempts to discredit Lamarckians by pointing to certain examples, such as the practice of circumcision or the former binding of feet by the Chinese, are also absurd and invalid for the same reason.

Another phenomenon that concurs more closely with the use concept of Lamarckian theory is that of *vestigial organs* (the human vermiform appendix, for example). Such atrophied organs are likely the result of *disuse*, and eventually may even disappear; and this is clearly not due to random mutation. To state it another way: in Lamarckism "use" is to the evolution and preservation of organs what "disuse" is to the atrophy of organs.

Homology

Another difficulty for the random mutation concept is the phenomenon of homology. *Homology* refers to two findings: (1) that the same organ may be revealed in many different animals of varying form and function and often from separate ancestry (e.g., the inner ear of the frog as compared to that of the human) and (2) that a nonidentical organ or feature on one animal may have an identical or similar function to some other organ or feature in an unrelated animal (e.g., homologous forelimbs of the bird, the bat, the porpoise, and the human, with each having certain key bones in identical relation to each other).

The evolution of eyes is considered one of the most outstanding examples of homology. Although the eyes of cephalopod mollusks—like squids and octopi—those of mammals, and those of insects have evolved independently along isolated lines for hundreds of millions of years, nonetheless the resemblances in appearance, properties, and function of this organ in such disparate lines is striking indeed. Whereas the similarities of the cephalopodal and mammalian eyes (including human eyes) are most remarkable, and although the compound eyes of the insects are less striking in resemblance to the others, nonetheless the insect eye works on exactly the same chemical basis as the two other types of eye. All of them focus light upon a substance in the retina known as retinol, which triggers the nerve impulses carried to the brain.[27]

Homologies pose an obvious problem for the mutation-selection theory, because they directly threaten the fundamental concept of randomness. Such recurrent commonalities and relationships in unrelated creatures bring certain fundamental principles to mind. "These fantastic resemblances have arisen independently from each other, but no science fiction creature, no bug-eyed monster, was produced by random mutations."[28]

In answer to the homological criticism, Darwinists have responded with the claim of "evolutionary constraints" that may operate in shaping evolution. But this would imply much more than simple randomness—such as the operation of wider principles of organization or directedness—and instead of a defense, may be viewed as an admission of inadequacy by Darwinists. Darwinists also claim that due to natural selection certain types of mutations may be more useful than others, and they tend to be preserved across species and to repropagate themselves. But this is also in direct contradiction to the pure-randomness concept and is once again an example of the *a posteriori*/redundancy fallacy. As the neurophysiologist Sherrington asked, "How is it then that man doesn't have six limbs like the insects, one pair [being] a set of wings?"[29]

Coevolution

Coevolution refers to the joint evolution of two or more species that have a close ecological relationship but do not exchange genes. Their coevolution has entailed more or less simultaneous alterations in each species in parallel fashion over time.

The most common examples of coevolution can be found in the interactions between insects and their food plants. Insects have one or more generations each year, and most food plants are annuals or biennials, with one generation each year or one every other year. Some species of the plant *Acacia*, for example, are mutually interdependent with certain types of ants. Whereas the ants feed on the plants, the plants are protected from other herbivores since the ants actively defend the leaves and will ferociously attack other insect species in the vicinity. In turn, *Acacias* have evolved nectaries and swollen thorns that attract and in turn benefit the ants.

Coevolutionary relationships may be found among many diverse species and environments. Other examples of nature's "odd couples" include: the sea anemone and the hermit crab (the sea anemone's stinging cells protect the crab, while the crab finds food for its guardian); tickbirds and the wart hog (while the wart hog's back furnishes food and shelter for the birds, the birds provide the hog with warning cries when danger approaches); algae and fungi (known as *lichen* and often found on rocks, the algae provide food for the fungi, while the fungi provide water for the algae).

The problems that coevolution pose for Darwinian theory are great. In a recent paper titled "Ecological Consequences of a Coevolved Mutualism Between Butterflies and Plants," zoologist Lawrence E. Gilbert acknowledges that "animal-plant mutations have been extensively described and yet, to date, we have no clear understanding of the great ecological and evolutionary importance of such interactions."[30] He notes that, at best, such intricate mutualisms are presently little more to biologists than an "interesting curiosity."

But they are much more than a curiosity—they are virtually impossible to understand or explain simply by the magical Darwinian premises of competition, random selection, and mutation. Whereas the evolution of a single species by Darwinian principles is almost totally impossible (as discussed above), the coevolution of two or more species compounds the improbability. The chances of random mutations affecting exact, correspondent genes of two or more species in simultaneity over long phases of numerous coordinated evolutionary transformations is incredibly unlikely.

Further, it is noteworthy that in almost every major text on the subject of evolution, Darwinian scientists rarely address themselves to this curious dilemma. At best they discuss coevolution as having resulted from natural selection (but that is insufficient in and of itself), and they dwell on the phenomenon of competition: that somehow, this coevolution of two mutually dependent species simply developed as the result of competitive battle. Such alleged "interspecific competition" has even been described as a "giant evolutionary game in which moves alternate with countermoves."[31]

This is what happens when advocates of an already false theory attempt to stretch its concepts to explain something that in essence is the exact opposite of what the premise (competition) implies. Trying to explain mutual interdependency (i.e., cooperation) on the basis of competition is at best an absurdity. This is reflected in an article that appeared in *Science Digest* ("Made for Each Other" by Rachel Wilder), describing the fascinating coevolutionary relationship between vampire bats and the banana flower. After recognizing that it took "millions of years for this intricate bat-plant relationship to evolve" Wilder turns to a wild extrapolation and declares that the human species evolved from anaerobic bacteria by a very long series of "beneficial" DNA errors.[32] She then turns to biologist Lewis Thomas to back up her claim, quoting his statement, "The capacity to blunder slightly is the real marvel of DNA. Without this attribute we would still be anaerobic bacteria, and there would be no music."[33] (It might also be said that the "real marvel" of biologists is *their* capacity to blunder, as in statements like those produced by Thomas and Wilder.)

Human Evolution

Although Darwinism's theoretical blind alleys can sometimes be bypassed in the realm of plants and animals, they blatantly dead-end in accounting for human behavior and, ultimately, human evolution. Alfred Wallace, Darwin's codiscoverer of natural selection, admitted as much when he said that unusual "over-developments," as exemplified in the extreme in the human brain and mind, far beyond the demands of survival, were indelible evolutionary questions that neither he nor Darwin could answer.[34]

Darwinian theory likewise has nothing to offer in explaining experience or human consciousness. Yet consciousness has evolved as much as any other characteristic of the human species.

Other curiosities emerge when Darwinism's less than convincing logic on animal evolution is extended to the human. Obvious contradictions to "selective value" (i.e., Darwinian survival mechanisms) that cannot be trimmed to fit the selectionists' quasi–theories are simply not addressed by them. Thus, the fact that in modern civilization the most developed individuals and predominant groups tend to produce the fewest offspring is given silence, as is the fact that many of these same people have historically ministered to the needs of the deprived, the sick, and the mentally ill. Darwinian genetic theory maintains that human struggle, both creative and destructive, has no transforming effect on the germ plasm, being an effect of random mutation. Accordingly, the highest ideals of civilization are seen by the selectionists as little more than temporary froth on the current of historical struggle, rather than cream rising to the top of the cultural churn. Arthur M. Young in *The Reflexive Universe* underlines this point: "In terms of present genetic theory, we might just as well omit civilization, life, work, careers, just put our seed into bottles and send it to the breeder. We ourselves are not even as useful as cattle, who do produce meat and dairy products."[35]

And if we are to carry the synthetic theory of evolution to its logical limit, we might consider what it would take to further evolve the human species. In order to produce an actual evolutionary transformation, besides through selective breeding, it would follow that we should have to begin to produce mutants by exposing people to radiation, much as the Darwinian experimenters have attempted to do with fruit flies. Strangely enough, this idea is actually entertained in a recent, acclaimed book, *The New Evolutionary Timetable*, in which author and neo-Darwinist Steven M. Stanley predicts that *Homo sapiens* will not likely evolve any further—unless there is a nuclear war that might leave some small, genetically altered groups of people who might comprise a new species.

In considering the facts of evolution there are two additional problems that are difficult for Darwinists to handle (or for any theory of evolution to handle, for that matter). The first is what may be referred to as *devolution*. Devolution occurs when a species stops evolving—that is, the life form has today the same anatomy, physiology, and behavioral instincts that it had displayed for many thousands or millions of years. This tends to hold true for most plant and animal species in existence today. In fact it may be that very few species (e.g., humans, dolphins) still have the flexibility and potential to evolve. Whether this is true or not is open to question, but the problem remains—why have so many plant and animal species remained unchanged for so many thousands or millions of years? If Darwinism were true, you might expect periodic transformations (i.e., evolution) in most species to occur during these long periods just by, in their view, the operation of statistical probabilities alone.

The Darwinists counter with the view that mutations may in fact have occurred over these vast periods of time but that it was not necessary for natural selection to come into play, simply because these species had found their niche, were comfortable in it, and had no need to "improve." Perhaps, but consider why moles can't see, why lizards don't fly, or why the elephant can't move any faster. Surely they have had time to evolve these traits, and certainly these traits would have aided their survival. Apparently, other factors are involved, and a more comprehensive explanatory perspective is needed.

Another problem for Darwinists (and again, for all evolutionary theorists as well) relates to the question of *why evolution occurs at all.* In actuality, from a strict Darwinian position, evolution *per se* makes absolutely no sense. With survival, adaptability, fecundity, variability, and the like considered as fundamental in the life process, it would suffice for any true Darwinian that, provided the species in question was surviving well enough within its niche, there would be no need to evolve. And of course this is exactly the case for most species of plants and animals that have survived unchanged after millions of years. If anything, Darwinian theory is more a theory of *devolution* than evolution.

The bottom line on Darwinism is nowhere better expressed than by Owen Barfield, where he notes that "the concept of chance is precisely what a hypothesis is devised to save us from." That is, the two— chance and hypothesis—are mutually exclusive. Barfield points out that the fervent disciples of Darwin cast their theories in terms inherently laden with both lingual and logical contradictions: "Because it is something we can do in the water, drowning should be included as one of the different ways of swimming."[36]

In sum, it is apparent that Darwinism in all its forms—including the "modern synthesis"—is wholly inadequate as a theory of evolution. It offers much in terms of explaining adaptation, reproductivity, survival, and population demographics, but that is the extent of it. It is a *misplaced* theory; it incessantly discusses evolution, but it is almost always referring to something else. To compound matters, the Darwinists as a whole are too obsessed to acknowledge this. They are like the man who refuses to step outside for fresh air because he is afraid he won't like the view. Not even all of his neighbors can convince him that it is not so bad.

Another limitation to the Darwinian doctrine is that it restricts itself to conventional life forms—plants, animals, and humans. Although this is not a major shortcoming, since most scientific theories tend to limit themselves to circumscribed phenomena, it may still be considered a weakness, since research is continually revealing that evolutionary processes appear to be (and have been) occurring at all known levels of material analysis—from atoms to galaxies. And if we accept these findings (as most scientists do), then it becomes difficult to envision what role accidental genetic mutations or natural selection would play at these other levels.

A truly unified theory will attempt to utilize more comprehensive concepts in accounting for evolution, since evolution appears to extend beyond the conventionally attributed life forms. But to arrive at a greater comprehension we need to look through neglected windows that the Darwinists long ago curtained off to us. In a sense, and true to their own beliefs, Darwinists have been successful at their own survival simply by "selecting out" anything that has not been in accordance with their position. But as already pointed out, flat obsession with survival and competition can only lead to devolution, or, at best, the status quo. Since we are, however, interested in evolution, including the evolution of our own thinking about evolution, the time is now ripe to consider new, or neglected, possibilities.

Chapter Eight

WHOLE CLOTH

While we orbit our way dynamically around them, Earth's creatures, from armadillos to spiders, live their own dynamic lives and display every kind of geometry from their studded hides to their symmetric webs. Even flowers ... have a flowing geometry closely analogous to the dynamic motion of the simplest of forms—forms that are naturally fluid and alive, and that epitomize the symmetry that seems to be the beginning of being.

Guy Murchie,
The Seven Mysteries of Life

The sight of a feather in a peacock's tail, whenever I gaze at it, makes me sick!

Charles Darwin
(Letter to Asa Gray, 1860)

Mother Nature, enchantress of evolution, has provided us with exceedingly beautiful sights to behold—patterns, order, design, and systems in all forms of life. These designs are the result of Mother Nature's "diagrammatic forces"—forces that have produced such wonders as the patterns on butterfly wings, the shapes of seashells, and the architecture of flowers. These salient characteristics of nature are wholly pervasive, predominant, and magnificent. Underlying these beauteous designs are exquisite principles encompassing mathematics and geometric form.

Darwinism, in its emphasis upon accident (e.g., genetic "mutilations"), fortuitous selection, and competition, has effectively distracted us from those features of nature that, to anyone with eyes to see, suggest a totally different picture. Whereas accidents and genetic mutations sometimes do happen, the effects of these random events are usually inconsequential or are compensated for. Although natural selection, or the fortuitous weeding out of the weak or unfit, also occurs, this typically is an ongoing ancillary phenomenon and, in general, all or most members of a given species tend to procreate on an equal basis: the weak as well as the strong survive.

Unblinkered observation further reveals that competition is only one small aspect of life and ecosystems, whereas cooperation and the smooth, mutual interaction of systems is much more prevalent. Members within a species rarely compete perpetually, and interracial/interspecies competition or battle is not the rule. (The human species might be considered an anomalous exception, although competition and war among humans are not necessarily universal or even the rule.) Animals, for example, destroy foliage only for food, and the predator-prey interaction generally occurs for the same reason. The "law of the jungle" or "dog eat dog" is more a pathological quirk found in some human societies; it certainly is not widespread throughout the plant and animal kingdoms. Peace overridingly prevails.

The universe as a whole, and all its subunits of galaxies, planetary systems, societies, organismic systems, organs, molecules, and atoms, as well as all their multilevel interactions, suggests a grand-scale ecosystem composed of numerous, mutually cooperative subsystems, all interconnected and reciprocal according to natural laws characterized by their almost divine simplicity, harmony, and beauty.

Modern brain research tells us that we are actually two brains in one—a right hemisphere and a left hemisphere—each serving very different (yet interactive) functions. The left brain specializes in logical, verbal, sequential, symbolic, and analytical functions. The right brain is more holistic, working to provide us with perceptions, intuitions, nonverbal processes, "illogic," and nonsequential activities. Our contemporary societies and educational systems have tended to overtrain our left brain, with comparatively little attention given to the right. It is no mere coincidence that the left brain is known as the dominant lobe, with the right considered the minor lobe. Left-brain analysis has also predominated, with society placing great value upon specialization. Specialization, we are told, is the key to success. Unfortunately, specialization too easily precludes comprehensive thinking. Buckminster Fuller, a comprehensive thinker in his own right, observes, "All universities have been progressively organized for even finer specialization. Society assumes that specialization is natural, inevitable, and desirable," yet he notes that "over-specialization is unnatural": "Nothing seems to be more prominent about human life than its wanting to understand all and put everything together."[1] So, although it may be that we all have a natural proclivity to understand and think comprehensively, our technological societies and educational systems have endeavored to push us in the other direction toward fragmentation. This may account for the popularity of Darwinism and its (anomalous) conception of a world composed mainly of competition and accident. Fortunately the focus is shifting. We are now beginning to realize that we can in fact get in touch with our right brain and use our whole brain to gain a more comprehensive, synthesized view of our universe.

Let us examine some of the key features that characterize this new world view, which has already been commonplace for millennia within certain ancient Eastern esoteric circles of thought.

MICRO/MACROCOSM

As above ... so below.

Hermes, *The Threefold Sage*

The universe and everything within it is interrelated. Like the proverbial Chinese box of objects reproduced within objects, such relationships remain constant, but within larger and larger (or smaller and smaller) levels of order. Although this interrelationship is difficult to describe and even more difficult to comprehend, it is in fact modular—with everything standing in relationship to everything else in a hierarchical continuum. The idea is utilized in General Systems Theory (Von Bertalanffy), in the idea of "holons" (Koestler), and in hologramic theory (Pribram and Leonard).

In discussing his idea of the modular universe, Itzhak Bentov (*Stalking the Wild Pendulum*) notes that human beings are units on an infinite scale of consciousness. As such, our collective mind functions as a focal point of manifest reality. Microcosm and macrocosm, material and immaterial, base and sublime—all are synthesized and unified by human consciousness. As atomic and subatomic research has shown, the focal point or unit blurs into the periphery of the one immediately below or above it, so much so that in atomic and molecular physics the human observer is sorely taxed in attempting to delineate where one level leaves off and the next begins.

Concerning the morophological nature of this hierarchy, Bentov sketches an important principle of the recurrence of form. The structure of the atom, the "original building block" of the universe, is repeated in the form of the solar system, and even more so in that of an elliptical galaxy, but only after passing through numerous intermediate hierarchical stages. Micro and macro mirror each other, at least to the human eye that views them.[2]

We are but small parts of something larger, which in turn makes up something even larger, *ad infinitum*. Like ourselves in the universe, our bodies are made up of many, many smaller parts—systems that function at once independently yet interdependently within ourselves, in a kind of prescribed autonomy.

HOLONOMY

If yonder raindrop its heart disclose,
Behold therein a hundred seas displayed.
In every atom, if thou gaze aright,
Thousands of reasoning beings are contained.

Shabistari,
13th Century[3]

In the photographic method of holography, a three-dimensional image is reproduced that retains its overall constancy at any level of analysis. A faithful production of the whole image is reproduced at every level. So, if the image plate is cut in half, a full reproduction appears in each part; and if cut in fourths again, a full reproduction appears; and in eighths, in sixteenths, and so forth, always we find a faithful reproduction in every individual part. Holography serves as a good analogical model to describe how life forms are organized as systems within systems. It is already known that every cell contains all the genetic material necessary to represent all features of the entire organism and that thousands of cells are lost and replaced with identical cells every minute. This is accomplished at the genetic level by way of the continuously occurring process of mitosis (cell division), with overall relationships always remaining constant.

The human brain is perhaps the epitome of the hologram as metaphor and concrete reality alike. In physical dimension it seems to be roughly midway between microcosm and macrocosm (atom and universe). Its function of mind has probed both as it seeks an answer to the mystery of the polarity of the vast and the infinitesimal. It seeks to unify, to make meaning of the dimensional disparity. To aid in this Promethean mental task it is reconciling metaphor with measurement once again, as was accomplished in the ancient world. The scientist and the mystic are rediscovering that their differences are mainly in method, not in substance. The divisions of the brain were intended by nature to be complementary rather than contradictory.

We are on the way to understanding, then, that the extraordinary functional specializations of the brain are matched only by its vast powers of synthesis. In order to have evolved this great capacity, it has developed a mode of receiving and reflecting the outer world that is unique in earthly biology, if in magnitude alone. Apprehension, comprehension, cognition, precognition, imagination, logical reasoning—these are the components of consciousness in which are rooted humankind's faith and fear, but it may yet refine these to a new definitive experience. If, as Leonard and the holonomists maintain, the hologram proves the primacy of design as an ultimate quality beyond the externalities of form, it is a short step to considering form itself, at least as we are used to thinking about it, as a quite secondary matter. The hologram reveals the *interior*, that which is inaccessible to the naked senses. The further we go, the fuzzier the edges become, whether of atomic particles or receding galaxies. If put at the same magnitude they may even be indistinguishable. Pattern takes on a more paramount meaning, size and extension rendered as beguiling superficialities. How then do we categorize? New modes of perception are demanded for understanding, transmuting both intellect and emotion. The quest for unity advances.

Though science has opened a few windows on the holographic phenomenon, it remains provocatively enigmatic in many of its aspects. None of these is so striking as its straightforward parallel to the brain. One brain cell functionally reflects the operations of the entire brain in the same way that a sliver of holographic plate contains the diminutized image of the whole plate. Similarly, the brain may well be a hologram of the earth, mirroring its essential systems and living dynamics.[4]

As you may recall, all living things were made ultimately from stars, thus tracing our atoms back to their origins in the heavens. This jibes with ancient, mystical conceptions, which are on record as stating that humankind's origins are "from far away," that we arrived here from "beyond the stars." Leonard, in broaching the subject of holonomy and its implications for human understanding, stresses that the technically prosaic modern mind has difficulty in accepting that a stone, seed, person, or grain of sand contains the cosmos. Yet the general realization of this ultimate connection, he says, must be part of the next step of conscious human evolution, adding that "in the hologram, we see science once again imitating mysticism, presenting us with a modern device which helps explain an ancient truth."[5]

HOLONS

Possibly one of the most effective efforts to counter the Darwinian (materialistic-mechanistic-reductionist) regression comes from Arthur Koestler in his discussion of holarchies and holons in his book *Janus: A Summing Up*. He refers to neo-Darwinism and behavioral psychology as being guilty of the "reductionist fallacy"—in the former's case, the tendency to reduce all of evolution to "the outcome of 'nothing but' chance mutations retained by natural selection" and in the latter, the tendency to reduce all of human behavior to "nothing but" a chain of conditioned reflexes.[6] He notes that this fallacy is easy for scientists to commit, since it is their task to "analyze complex phenomena into their constituent elements." However, it is too easy for them to forget that "in the course of their analyses something essential is always lost, because the whole is always more than the sum of its parts, and its attributes as a whole are more complex than the attributes of its parts." Koestler considers this "world-view of reductionist orthodoxy" to be restrictive, and notes that to take this reductionist orthodoxy at face value would be to say that humanity itself is nothing more than a fleshly bag of 90 percent water and 10 percent minerals. Chemically, this evaluation is quite true, but, as Koestler dubs it, "not very helpful."[7]

In attempting to go beyond mere reductionism and even holism, Koestler has developed an outline for a system he refers to as a holarchy. A *holarchy* is a hierarchical system of holons, where a *holon* refers to a sublevel or "subwhole" (an integrated, autonomous system in its own right) within the total hierarchal system. In considering living systems, Koestler advances Bentov's ideas but emphasizes the integrated, semiautonomous nature of each biological unit in the hierarchy, or holarchy. Cells, nerves, muscles, and organs all have specialized modes of functioning, so that under observation each appears as a quasi-independent realm within the larger structure it serves. Though we may not go so far as to liken this organization across the board to a social one, many metaphors are obviously there.

Koestler refers to each realm as being "Janus-faced," in that it is servitor to a higher whole above itself while yet sustaining its own constituencies below. King and subjects, state and citizen, autocracy or democracy, the similes abound.

Koestler notes that the idea of an emergent, multileveled hierarchy goes against the materialistic *Zeitgeist*, because it implies that the biological laws that govern life are qualitatively different from those laws of physics that govern inanimate matter—that life cannot simply be reduced to the "blind dance of atoms."

SYNERGY

Synergy is a concept similar in basis to Koestler's holons; and to borrow from him it might also be referred to as the *Janus principle*. The term *synergy*, first coined by scientist-thinker-inventor R. Buckminster Fuller, is defined as "unique behaviors of whole systems unpredicted by any behaviors of their component functions taken separately."[8] For example, the stable structural behavior of water (H_2O) is not predictable from a mere analysis of its component parts, hydrogen and oxygen; the emergence of a new product, water, *is synergetic*—i.e., emergent. Synergy is an integral concept within the school of thought known as General Systems Theory—a comprehensive, interdisciplinary movement founded by biologist Ludwig von Bertalanffy. Its purpose is to develop theoretical models and discover general principles that are "universally applicable to biological, social and symbolic systems of any kind—in other words, a search for common denominators in the flux of phenomena, for unity-in-diversity."[9]

DINERGY

With little here to do or see
Of things that in the great world be,
Sweet Daisy! oft I talk to thee,
For thou art worthy,
Thou unassuming Common-place
Of Nature, with that homely face,
And yet with something of a grace,
Which Love makes for thee!

William Wordsworth,

The Daisy[10]

"Dinergy" is a new term coined by Gyorgy Doczi in his illuminating book *The Power of Limits: Proportional Harmonies in Nature, Art and Architecture.* Dinergy is made up from two Greek words: *dia*—meaning "across, through, opposite," and *energeia*—"energy." Dinergy or dinergic energy is the "creative energy of organic growth." It relates to the dynamic and synergetic union of opposites, which is an essential characteristic of the pattern-forming process found in the development and structure of all life forms. In his book Doczi brilliantly documents the pattern-forming process as it occurs in nature, as well as how nature is reflected in art, architecture, and even lifestyles ("arts of living"). He graphically notes the pattern-forming process in such diverse life forms as plants, beetles, butterflies, shells, clams, crabs, fishes, even the dinosaur, and then notes this process reflected in a plethora of human activities, such as music, crafts (pottery, carpet making, basket weaving), and the design of airplanes.

It seems that we adults tend to develop a kind of psychic astigmatism that clouds our visionary sense of wonder at the incredible designs of beauty abounding in the world around us. As children we take notice of curious details: we want to know why a starfish has no head or tail, why an apple blossom always has five petals, why a spider's web looks so flimsy but is so strong. We wonder why we ourselves are like one thing and not like another. We experience limits and imagine limitlessness. We sense the harmonies, perfections, and beauty of this earth inviting us to even greater wonders just over the horizon.

These are the higher realms of mind that should lead us to our most fulfilling adventures in adulthood, not something to be outgrown. It is here that the frontiers of philosophy, art, religion, and science fade off into the encompassing horizons of intangible, unconditioned Reality. Heretofore avoided because of its immaterial and immeasurable nature, Doczi states that we must proceed to investigate Dinergy because "the powers that shape our lives have their source here."[11]

The most striking, and perhaps most profound, principles that fit diverse forms of life into relationship are those expressed mathematically as well as metaphorically and artistically. With these, our previously discussed abstractions can be verified by intellect and senses (visual and auditory) alike. But they are appreciated with the heart. In harmony and symmetry the lofty is linked to the mundane. The spiritually inclined make the connections instantly. Art is the produce of their inner elaborations. Even the most avant-garde, style-scuttling artists seek a *form* of expression, be it ever so radical and personal. The unknown is what is sought and, if a coherent method of seeking it is lacking, the artwork generally loses its meaning for everyone except the self-indulgent artist. It then represents aesthetic bankruptcy— abstraction at its unrelated worst.

Artists are the pioneers in the frontier of unexperienced form. They work their materials into new designs, exploring, discovering, consolidating, expanding, and finally dissolving the old into the new. The parallels with natural chemistry, molecular biology, genetics, and evolution itself need no belaboring. Dynamic design is the common denominator. However, only very recently have scientists as a group begun to appreciate the immense intricacies of the designs outside of their own particular specialties.

The ancients were indubitably our masters in combining mathematics and metaphor in a fully human balance. Their law, religion, philosophy, art, and science are the rich evidence. We have more technical knowledge, but without their earth-wisdom it is a double-edged sword, the sharpest edge of which is held against ourselves. The classical Greeks, Persians, Indians, Arabs, and others searched for proportions and found facts along the way. Western people have sought and hoarded facts alone and lost proportion—there are simply too many facts and too little room to store them in a present-day brain.

In geometry the Greeks discovered what must be the key cipher to decoding the infinities of revealed form. This is the *phi* (ø) ratio, or "golden mean," stated algebraically as $\frac{AB}{BC} = \frac{BC}{AC}$.

To arrive at *phi*, a line (*AC*) is divided at a single point, yielding two unequal segments. The smaller one (*AB*) is proportionate to the larger one (*BC*) as the larger one (*BC*) is to the whole line.

Thus, the *phi* point would occur as *B* on this line:

A	*B*	*C*

There can be only one *phi* point on a given line. A line will yield a curve (logarithmic) called the "golden spiral" when it connects the *phi* points of a series of progressively smaller rectangles derived from the largest. The *T'ai chi* (yin-yang) symbol is such a golden spiral. Digited, the "golden ratio" is 1:1.618 ... to infinity.

The golden ratio is a unique proportion in that it is the only irrational (not amenable to an exact figure) number that can be subdivided endlessly. As such it is an *a priori* validation of the holarchy idea we discussed. Quantitatively, it is an ultimate symbol of the eternal and limitless possibilities of consciousness (e.g., ideas). Geometrically, it relates points in space and crystallizes design.

Plato's Theory of Forms, as represented by the hierarchal pyramid of Ideas, reached for the same truth, but the logarithmic curve or golden spiral is a better mathematical fit to a curved universe.

Renaissance artists such as da Vinci, Titian, and Raphael made profuse use of the golden ratio to create masterpieces of exquisite symmetry. If later modern artists thought this preoccupation with symmetry unnatural, modern botany and zoology stand to correct them. For the *phi* ratio occurs with abundant regularity throughout the plant and animal kingdoms. Evidently the classics and ancients were devoted seekers of connection.

An example of the golden ratio, as contained in the structure and design of the daisy, can be seen in the diagrams on page 85.[12]

Similar *phi* proportions are ubiquitous in nature, such as in the sunflower, apple blossom, garlic plant, nautilus. Doczi notes that "in patterns of organic growth the irrational ø ratio of the golden section reveals that there is indeed an infinite and intangible side to our world."[13]

TELEOLOGY

Teleology refers to "the study of final causes," especially in reference to material processes. The doctrine of mechanistics holds that all natural phenomena and the development of life forms result from random processes, but teleology is the belief that natural phenomena (while acknowledging the interaction in part of fortuitous events) are largely the result of overall design, plan, or purpose. The idea was first popularized by theologist-philosopher William Paley, in an effort to prove the existence of a Higher Power. If a watch, he asked, was an exquisite contrivance of engineering and function, didn't it pale beside the wondrous works that constituted its creator—namely the human being? And if the former could be issued into existence only by a purposeful intelligence, how could one possibly think of the latter as merely the most tricked-up creation of chance biology?

Although a full rehashing of teleological arguments is not necessary to expose the fallacies of the dogma of randomness in explaining evolved structure, such summary observations as those by Paley turn on the axis of the issue. Beyond this there is no further intellectual ground. Individuals can only decide the matter for themselves by personal or intuitive criteria, girded by their perceptual powers and grasp of the essential. They are then able to weigh truly the strengths and weaknesses of the various outlooks.

Those new to the field of evolution may have less difficulty in seeing the patterns than many who are already blinkered by the superimpositions typical of Darwinism. Word concepts all too often cloud the subject rather than clarify it. Scientific literacy may or may not promote new viewpoints and understanding, depending on the literati themselves. As we have seen, such literacy is formally impressive, though it is frequently unproductive. The effect is excellently illus-

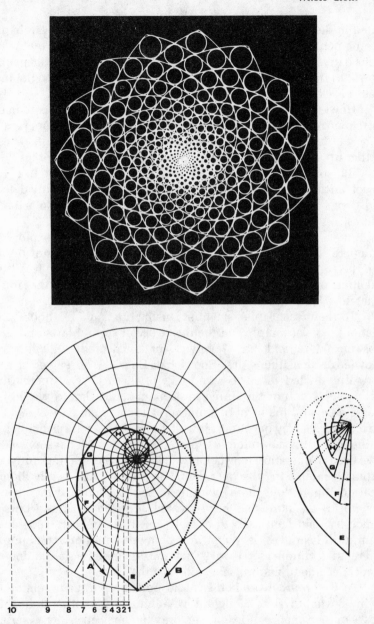

Diagrams of a daisy. The generating spirals move in opposite directions, are logarithmic (bottom left), and equiangular (bottom right).

trated in the Sufi tale of "The Ants and the Pen." In it an ant happens upon a pen producing fine calligraphy and is astonished by the enormous display of power and beauty. Oblivious to a higher dimension, he attributes the "squiggles on this beautiful surface" solely to the instrument he sees.

However, a second, more observant ant notices that "certain other objects surround it and drive it on its way." So the fingers are reckoned to be the forces of creation. But then another ant raises his eyes yet further up and perceives a hand. Surely this is the Prime Mover.

But soon enough the hand is discovered to be attached to a greater object (an arm), and that to a body. Another hand is presently detected, and then two legs and feet, which extend far beyond the activity of interest.

As the story ends the ants are still pursuing their explorations. Although yielding an acceptable mechanical explanation of the writing, their investigatory methods continue to fail to locate its ultimate intention and origin because, as the story concludes, the ants are "literate."

To the present time, scientists (using the "ant" method of investigation) have accomplished the discovery of several laws and principles of nature and have evolved (or uncovered) a sophisticated knowledge of mathematics. Books like Doczi's *The Power of Limits* have illuminated to us the workings of these laws, principles, and mathematics within the universe of nature. But should we desire to progress beyond the level of ant observation and study, we might first wish to ask the key question: How is it that these laws, principles, and mathematics arrived in the first place? After all, they have existed and have been in operation long before we, through painstaking study, were fortunate enough to "discover them," as we say. And surely there is a great deal more "out there" waiting to be discovered. If the universe, our world, or nature has been created according to these laws and principles, and continues to operate and run smoothly according to them, it ill behooves us to continue along the lines of ant assumption and relative blindness to invoke such sterile sophistries as randomness, chance, accident, natural selection, and the like.

As Guy Murchie and other philosophers continue to remind us, a divine power, mystery, delight, love—and a host of other unquantifiables—are personal realities proven only by themselves, by experience. Even scientific terms such as *randomness* hint at something ultimately unprovable by strictly scientific means. The phenomena encompass the discipline, not vice versa.

I am told by mathematicians that the randomness of larger, complex numbers, generally speaking, is not provable.... Whatever or

Whoever directs the mysterious forces of life and evolution has not yet come fully under the wing of science and is more than liable to be misjudged—if for no reason than that randomness always implies some degree of mystery, while mystery for its part does not necessarily imply any degree of randomness.[15]

The magnificence of our universe, whether "out there" or in our heads, should assist in opening our minds to the situation confronting us. In trying to understand ourselves, life, the universe, and evolution, we should keep in mind that the scope is immense and never-ending.

It is easy to mistake the part for the whole, as does Darwinism, and a more comprehensive view may now be better appreciated. Evolution deals with vast and intricate ecological relationships between life forms of varying size and scale both outside and inside the organism. Within the organism, trillions of cells are in continual contact and communication, all working in concert. Science is still in its infancy in its attempt to understand these remarkable phenomena, and undoubtedly many wonders await discovery. The manifestation of design, pattern, and mathematical principles in nature calls for an expanded view of ourselves and our potentials—a view that can help us understand evolution as a much more wondrous process than recognized hitherto.

Chapter Nine

TRANSFORMISM

The legends of many peoples are full of changing-into-something-else not unlike what the butterfly takes for granted. Ovid's Metamorphoses—by no means an entomological work—is one of the most enduringly popular books ever written. The impossible possibility that a man or even a beast might turn into some wholly different creature seems to fascinate something buried deep in human nature.

Joseph Wood Krutch,
The Great Chain of Life

Everything living—from the smallest of insects to the highest holders of consciousness—remembers. Life remembers prior to itself; life inherits memories, both conscious and subconscious. According to *transform-ism*—or the theories of Goethe, Lamarck, and Butler—this is the most important aspect of evolution.

Although Goethe did not outline a formal theory of evolution, the idea of transformism—or intentional and systematic, as opposed to accidental, transmutation—is found throughout his writings on biology and nature. Seemingly influenced by Plato's theory of Universals, Goethe was transfixed by uniformities and commonalities in nature; he felt that all forms developed from an "ideal type," or structural plan, that was not visible in the ordinary world. He referred to this ideal type as an *Urphanomenon* (primal phenomenon): "There is nothing higher than they [primal phenomena] among visible things, but they on the other hand are wholly suited to permit us to descend from them, step by step, to the commonest instance of daily experience."[1] Goethe found no agreement with the reductionistic, analytic approach to nature so common in conventional science, rather favoring an approach that is just now—300 years later—coming into vogue, known as holism. For him, an analytical relationship with nature, dealing with "single mate-rial parts," was as impoverished as it was absurd. To not "feel the breathing of the spirit" in the manifestation of natural laws, he felt, led to a science that was most unnatural.[2]

Goethe was interested in biological growth and development, and especially in morphology (shape and formation) and transformation. He wrote of "centrifugal" and "centripetal" forces inherent in nature that worked to produce morphologic form. Among the many "myste-rious forces" in nature he felt awaited human discovery, one of the most mysterious and most important related to the phenomenon of metamorphosis.

> Always changing, firm persisting,
> Near and far and far and near,
> Thus in forming and transforming—
> To your wonder I am here.[3]

Although Goethe's writings on nature as a whole are aligned with trans-formism, his understanding of evolution, while always implied, was rarely elaborated upon. At best, for example, we find the following taken from his diary: in September 1797, in a conversation with the Tübingen professor K. F. Kielmeyer, the hypothesis was introduced "that the higher organisms in their development advance by a few stages which leave the others behind."[4]

The first modern theory of evolution based upon transformism is that of Jean Baptiste Lamarck (1809), later amplified and expanded upon by Samuel Butler (1878). Although Lamarck appeared to limit his ideas to the same range of conventional life forms as did Darwin (plants, animals, humans), Butler extended his views to other realms, considering *everything* to be alive—a true theory of universal evolution.

Although Lamarck's views were first published in 1809 in his book *Philosophie Zoologique*, a more complete exposition of his theory was provided in 1815 in his classic, seven-volume *Invertebrate Zoology* (or *Histoire naturelle des Animaux sans Vertebres*), completed in Paris in 1822. The bulk of his discussions centered upon the evolution of animals, with occasional references to plants and humans. The late H. Graham Cannon, the leading modern spokesman on Lamarckism, in his book *Lamarck and Modern Genetics* summarizes Lamarck's basic theory by paraphrasing Lamarck's four basic laws:

> *First Law*: Life, by its own force, tends continually to increase the volume of every living body and to extend the dimensions of its parts, up to a limit which it imposes.
>
> *Second Law*: The production of a new organ in an animal body results from a need [*besoin*] which continues to make itself felt, and from a new movement that this need brings about and maintains.
>
> *Third Law*: The development and effectiveness of organs are proportional to the use of those organs.
>
> *Fourth Law*: Everything acquired or changed during an individual's lifetime is preserved by heredity and transmitted to that individual's progeny.[5]

The first law is of least importance to us, as it has been for others. It basically implies that as we move up the phylogenetic scale of evolution there will tend to be a progressive increase in physical size of the species in general. Lamarck based his reasoning on the idea that with increased movement or activity organs will increase in size. Although his reasoning here is incorrect, since organisms lower on the phylogenetic scale are also quite active, his conclusion is generally true since as we move up the phylogenetic scale there is a tendency for organisms to grow in size and, more generally, in complexity.

The second law is important because of the idea of *need*. Need refers both to environmental demands and internal needs (usually both at once).

The third law refers to organ *use* (and conversely, disuse), implying that organ development or loss of development (i.e., atrophy) is contingent on use of that organ.

The fourth law, which has caused the most controversy, is commonly referred to as the *principle of the inheritance of acquired characteristics*. Simply put, this law implies that environmental and internal needs (second law) in conjunction with the related use of some given organ (third law) will lead to increased development of that organ, with these effects impressed into the heritable substrate of the organism and transmitted to its offspring.

This law has come under attack for several reasons, but (up until very recently) the major criticism has been that no evidence exists for any physiological *mechanism* (or mechanisms) within the organism that would allow for this phenomenon to actually take place.

For Lamarck, there existed a primeval force that "tends incessantly to complicate organization," and he believed that the drive toward perfection was inherent in the total evolutionary process. Samuel Butler fully accepted Lamarck's views and extended and strengthened them with his own observations.

In his book *Unconscious Memory*, Butler sets forth his first important principle, that the definitions of "living" (organic) and "non-living" (inorganic) are too arbitrary. Straightaway, he proposes to "start with every molecule as a living thing, and then deduce death as the breaking up of an association or corporation." The putative inorganic realm should be "regarded as up to a certain point living, and within certain limits, with consciousness, volition, and power of concerted action."[6]

This is a bold premise. However, contemporary science in some respects has adduced evidence along these same lines. For example, a Chinese physicist, Madame Wu, in describing the experiments of her two Nobel Prize-winning associates (C. N. Yang and T. D. Lee) on the conservation of parity, announced that "cobalt, in its observed radioactivity, is aware of a future different from its past and it uses this fact in making a spatial distinction between its right and its left. It is capable of making a choice between these two directions."[7]

Butler reinforced the Lamarckian principle of need with the equally important one of *continuity*. This is where he alloyed Lamarckian theory into a more workable explanation of change, beyond anything Darwinism could hammer out with haphazard logic. Butler called the latter "the theory without a backbone," and for good reason; it has yet to adduce a credible mechanism of genetic alteration. Its logic, he charged, rendered "the progress of one generation...always liable to be cancelled and obliterated by that of the next." A theory that did have a backbone was one that recognized "the tolerably constant or slowly varying needs of large numbers of individuals for long periods together."[8]

The profound illogic of random mutation as a format for genetic transformation has been shown. Still, its adherents cling to it as an inexpert magician clings to magic potions, though they are producing nothing. Butler's insights were possible because in his time the search for a magic mechanism had not yet reached the Eureka! level of obsession. A similar fallacy is found in the story of the man who, though he has lost a key inside his own house, searches for it outside; when someone questions his method, he replies, "But there's more light out here."

Butler agreed with Lamarck that involved in all evolutionary change was need, which was to be found inside the organism. If need is defined in any sense other than the physical (hunger, sex, territoriality, etc.), it can provide a foundation and a framework for both. In this context what is called "instinct" is a special case in point. It is an elusive concept, fuzzy even when focused on particular aspects of behavior. Out of context, it clarifies nothing. We say, for instance, that a newborn infant cries by instinct, but that is little more meaningful than saying that, upon maturing, he grows to six feet by instinct. Though quite different processes, both are behaviors (activities), and instinct explains nothing in its ordinary usage.

On the other hand, Butler reasoned, what if such behaviors, functions, and, conceivably, habits were prelearned, not only in the womb but long before in what Lamarck had coined "inherited characteristics"? The idea of instinct could then begin to make some real sense. In his books *Life and Habit* and *Unconscious Memory* Butler did just that. Lamarck's conceptual lens was reground and much of the theoretical blur was resolved.

As is indicated by his titles, Butler believed that the habits and behaviors peculiar to different species were learned (or programmed) and strengthened with each successive generation—hence, *acquired* characteristics. Any kind of learning depends upon memory, and here at last is the obvious but unrecognized master-key. Memory is activated by need, the higher need being to transcend the prior level, to improve and refine the existing state of the race. Once survival is adequately ensured, the need is then to develop and elaborate characteristics essential to other, more advanced (and sometimes nonsurvivalist) levels.

To communicate this process in language, the terms must be enlarged so that the complexity can be encompassed. Butler applied memory to inorganic as well as organic phenomena where any entity repeated one option or "choice" over another for no reason necessarily connected to survival, by human reasoning at least. Innumerable features of life and the evolutionary process continue to be loose ends incapable of being tied together adequately with existing Darwinist theory. How can such a rationale, threadbare of context, be rewoven into an understanding of such elaborations as altruism, supraspecialization, and creativity? It all fits only in the context of a tracing back through inheritance, continuity, and need—in other words, ancestral to earliest, inorganic origins. And if we do not know where consciousness itself emerges, how can we know where life in reality begins? Who knows, therefore, how far into the primordial past a "human" trait has its precursors?

At this point it is useful to restate a conclusion of the last chapter, namely that design is preeminent throughout nature and that its interlinked patterns are the living blueprints of evolution. Having rejected random adaptation as a feasible mode for this blueprinting, we automatically face its only alternative: precedent purpose. Regardless of whether we are able to attribute the existence of design to an ultimate source or Creator, its very manifestation is irrefutable evidence for purposeful plan, even if it is nothing more than the functional necessity of a covert system in which design is only the visible facet.

In embarking on a discussion of the evolutionary mechanisms (or dynamics) put forth by Lamarck and Butler, we must appreciate the broader ranges of their ideas of organicity (life), memory, habit, instinct, inheritance, beyond the restricted, everyday meanings. Only then can the further subtleties such as need and continuity be understood as even more basic principles.

Butler stressed this necessity for revivifying the fuller definitions, for instance calling memory "an ultimate and original power, the source and at the same time the unifying bond, of our whole conscious life."[9] In like manner did he view everything material as evolving and therefore as alive. Reflecting on the two fundamental states of materiality and immateriality (invisible, unquantifiable) that constitute the relative essence of all phenomena, he foresaw realities only quite recently verified by scientific research.

Memory is a good point of departure in our deepening of the evolutionary concept. We usually think of it in patently human terms: the conscious, willful retrieval of fact and information. Outside of this it takes us into the shadowy psychic realms: night and day dreaming, associative imagery, hypnotic states, time distortion, in short all mental experience not properly called conscious. But antecedent to these two categories there is strong evidence for a more primordial memory— referred to by Carl Jung as the "collective unconscious"—in which both are grounded, which is not equatable to a fortuitous, mechanistic transmission of "instinct" from one generation to the next.

Lamarck and Butler's concepts are highly integrative. Several of their key terms are so closely related that they require an especially supple grasp on the reader's part to be wholly absorbed. Scientists themselves are increasingly being forced to reflect on this reemerging mode, due in main to the hard evidence of their research alone. Metallurgy, for example, might seem an unlikely field to bear out Butler's propositions, but a recent report by L. McDonald Schetby entitled "Shape-Memory Alloys," based on replicated findings, attributes "anthropomorphic qualities" of training and memory to a new generation of alloys. This "shape-memory effect" gives convincing evidence of a kind of preorganic, evolutionary impulsion toward more complex "behavior," far beyond the simple physical attributes of ductility, malleability, conductivity, tensile strength, and so forth.[10]

In the shape-memory alloys we see the early etching of an evolutionary design. But we must go back even further to see the very first squiggles, as it were, in subatomic life. We must recapitulate the outline of evolution.

Over immensities of time subatomic particles learned, by option or direction, to combine with other particles, remembered and repeated this intermeshing with still other particles, until the first (hydrogen) atom was formed. The same process occurred in the formation of other kinds of atoms, and certain ones of these went on to interact with differing atoms to form elements and molecules. Aggregations of molecules eventually formed, wherein we see organizational complexity that seems discriminatory almost in a social sense. Crystals and compounds resulted. It was at this level that biologists drew the attention of other specialists to the surprising capacity of all material forms for transmutation, beginning at the subatomic foundation (see *Biological Transmutations* by Louis C. Kervran[11]).

DNA/RNA, genes, and single-celled organisms at last evolved. The Lamarck/Butler principles of need, directed (perhaps "conscious") effort, and interplay of external pressures, transmutation, aggregation, learning, memory and trait inheritance increased in momentum and elaboration up the evolutionary ladder. Certain varieties of cells developed a rarefied capacity to recognize each other out of the alien crowd, aggregated and formed specialized tissues. Responding to internal and external (environmental) necessities, tissues arranged into organs, and these in turn formed organ systems. Finally, these systems integrated with other systems, and we have run the gamut from particle to biotic beginnings.

Normally, all activities of development, organization, and maintenance—at all levels—were under the direction of some centralized agency, such as the cell's nucleus or the higher organism's central nervous system.

It is essential to remember that the principal concepts being discussed are exclusively neither physical nor psychological. As research generally indicates, these two traditional categories are as arbitrary as they are useful. Most of the thinkers cited concur that there is no pin-pointed origin for life, just as anthropologists have been unable to iden-tify a singular forerunner for *Homo sapiens*. Likewise, consciousness is being divested of its strictly human identification.

Learning is the basic process by which these functions of mind (consciousness) are synthesized. We can call instinct cumulative, heritable impulses (including pregenetic transfer), the result of mem-ory associated with learning. Instinct manifests as acquired charac-teristics, internal reflexes, and innate behavior. For example, in an animal a limb forms through morphogenetic movement (behavior) of certain cells that, through memory of collective ("social") developmen-tal behavior, are able to form the needed organ.

But what directs this marvel of organization, an intelligent activity by definition? The gene, of course, is governor of the individual cell. But how is the specialized interplay of all these cells coordinated so that the organism adheres as a miraculous structure? An overall means of control must always be operating, turning genes on and off, directing and modulating activity. What is the omnipotent agent? The biogeneticists themselves have yet to isolate a Prime Mover. Some sci-entists, such as Dr. Roy Walford of UCLA's School of Medicine, have postulated a "supergene." Others are looking at bioelectrical fields and related entities in hopes of discovering the modus operandi.

The propensity for learning in humans is generally attributed to some nature/nurture ratio of environmental (i.e., socioeconomic, domestic, educational) factors and the quantitative inheritance of IQ. However, an "instinct to learn" and experience may also be passed on through the genes. In an article definitively entitled "The Instinct to Learn," biologists James L. Gould and Carol Grant Gould summed up the latest thinking in the field, which, curiously, substantiates Butler's views that were set forth a century ago, then virtually disregarded shortly thereafter. They cite numerous cases revealing that much ani-mal learning, though influenced by environmental factors, is "nonethe-less rigidly controlled by genetic programming." This genetically transmitted learning involves behaviors far more complex than simple instinctual responses, yet it is just as "immutable and stereotyped."

Neurobiological research is now tracking down the neural circuits involved in these behaviors, although, as the Goulds point out, the evidence is being contested by many scientists and humanists because it seems to counter the cherished concept of free will. However, they advise facing up to the fact that genetic impulses are strongly—per-haps predominantly—determinants of what we learn and that "even much of our 'culture' is deeply rooted in biology."[12]

So the capacity to learn certain things is genetically programmed or, in older parlance, instinctual. However, this programmed propensity for learning is a far cry from the Darwinian notion of instinct as an array of mindless compulsions, shaped by the random effects of mutation and nearly synonymous with slightly complex reflexes.

The instinct for learning develops only as an ongoing continuum. *Ipso facto*, it is a product of memory (or memory storage). By relieving this and other concepts of their impoverished reductionism, Butler did a needed service for biological theory and paved the way for a new synthetic view of mind, body, and evolution. His thought gave further dimension, and consequently meaning, to the idea of consciousness. He saw mind as being as fundamentally subject to investigation by the scientific method as matter was, a fact whose full import is just being realized. Moreover, he believed that these two sciences (biology and psychology) could eventually be united as one. He was among the first of Western thinkers to stress the complex interdependence of the material and the immaterial (which he called spiritual). His transformation theory of evolution was cornerstoned by the insight that this mutual interdependence between the spiritual and the material is itself dependent upon natural law.

It has taken formal physics several centuries of rigorous research to repeat the same conclusion. The "New Physics" is now very much with us. In his book *The Tao of Physics*, the new-physicist Fritjof Capra sums up:

> Quantum theory has abolished the notion of fundamentally separated objects.... It has come to see the universe as an interconnected web of physical and mental relations whose parts are only defined through their connections to the whole.[13]

But in the 19th century the truly eye-opening research had yet to be done. Transformation theory entered the evolutionary arena largely unheralded. Many scientists considered it an empirical underdog that stood no chance against the bulky argument of the Darwinists. Still, if the David did not slay Goliath, neither did it retreat into obscurity or illogic. In fact, Darwinism was a giant in little but dogma and publicity, and its proponents generally avoided a point-by-point public exchange with the Lamarckians, preferring rather to heap up their concoctions of proof before a scientifically untutored public. Debate, for the most part, was kept politely academic. Which is not to say that it did not openly erupt from time to time. Respected disciplinaries in fields as diverse as theosophy and theoretical physics (which together are now converging on common truths) periodically threw down the gauntlet on either side of the controversy and were widely published. The sparks of rebuttal and counterrebuttal from lesser authorities would then fly through tabloids, tracts, journals, and occasional verbal debates. At times the rearguard attacks were so misconstrued that they actually weakened the main thrusts of both camps.

In the late 1800s there were few more able spokesmen for the neo-Lamarckians than the renowned French philosopher Henri Bergson. In his classic *Creative Evolution*, Bergson reinforced the metaphysical base of transformism while adhering to scientific principles. He was especially interested in the phenomenon of homology, or the parallel development of identical organ systems in independently evolved species. Lacking any kind of sensible rationale for explaining this "convergence of effects," Darwinism struck him as being completely off the map in this area. On the other hand, the neo-Lamarckian focus on internal, psychological factors made possible an answer, in the way of effort or impetus. Bergson believed that only neo-Lamarckism could account for homological cases. "For," he wrote, "it is quite conceivable that the same effort to turn the same circumstances to good account might have the same result."[14]

Bergson is strongly echoing Butler's emphasis on internal motivation. He even uses the phrase "an inner directing principle" leading into his discussion. In other words, habit or behavior (i.e., psychology) is to be considered more important in evolution than the influence of the environment *per se*, as stressed by the Darwinians.

Here again, modern science vindicates Lamarck. Zoology has turned up a plethora of homologues (related structures) in widely divergent species that would have amazed and pleased Bergson himself. The growing consensus is that the development of many key internal and external physical structures has progressed independently of environmental conditions. Conversely, in a constant environment, different forms (or "races") of the same species often vary sharply in physical features, this being so because of differences in behavior patterns that *preceded* the change in structures.

Dolphins and whales provide striking instances of homology (for excellent discussion, see "Dolphins and the Mind of Man," by zoologist W. Tschernezky[15]). The cetaceans are extremely divergent in manner of feeding, migration, and internal structure. Yet we classify them primarily by their secondary characteristics relating to locomotion. "Mammals that live in the sea" is the pseudozoological description of whales, but cetologists know that it is not much more useful than calling canines "mammals that live on land." Indeed, Captain Scoresby in *Moby-Dick* says, "No branch of Zoology is so much involved as that which is entitled 'Cetology'."

With whales the "survival of the fittest" cannot be attributed mainly to fortuitous, mutational adaptation to the environment, since the great variety of whale structure has developed *since* geophysical stabilization of the oceans. Fish-eating dolphins, mammal hunters, squid-eaters, sperm whales, filtrating baleens, and many others are swimming success stories of broad specializations. Obviously, then, these forms in some way *actively opted* for different behaviors, not because they were competing for survival, but rather because they experimented with various modes of functioning while relatively flourishing. The wide radiation of structure was then in response to long-term deviations of habit, not environmental demands. By the latter logic—or probability "laws"—there would be only several, highly adapted, dominant forms. Such is far from the case, however. Out on the cetacean extremes are the blind dolphin, a river dweller, and the other-worldly sea unicorn.

It should be noted here that Lamarck, Butler, and Bergson by no means dismissed the environment as only a stage for a final, scripted extravaganza of evolution. On the contrary, it was the very theatre of nature, dynamic in essence, which provided both the format and the living stock for the drama. Without it there could be no performers in flesh. The "play" itself was planned, but it was acted out spontaneously and for an exalted purpose. One purpose was the transcendence of the natural environment, and it often played a central role as protagonist or antagonist to the drive toward higher life forms. This drive Bergson called the *élan vital*, or roughly, "immense wave," "current," "vital impetus." Most commonly viewed as originating at certain points among the stars, it magnetically connected to earth elements, interacted with matter and transformed it, gaining in intensity with each transformation. For Bergson it was the great giver and organizer of life.

Bergson's concept of creative evolution implies something more than just the "finalist" view that sees evolution as something unfolding according to a preconceived plan or design; this is too deterministic. Bergson holds somewhere between determinism (plan) and free will (creativity). Just as an artist is not completely sure in advance what his final product will be like, and just as the artistic process to a great extent entails the interplay of spontaneity and plan, so Bergson views the process of evolution in the same way. He sees evolution as "a creation increasingly renewed," which creates as it goes on. He sees this process as especially significant in the phenomenon of human evolution, where he notes that, for a conscious being, "to exist is to change, to change is to mature, to mature is to go on creating oneself endlessly."

We have now come back full circle to the axial principle of evolution that will be further elaborated in the next chapter: transmutational change, and its possible *modus operandi*(s). By definition change *is* mutation, or deviation from the established mode. Both Lamarck and Butler reasoned that all variations of structural form were precipitated by departure from habit, which in turn was prompted by an accelerating instinct through generations to break through the limitations of the old forms. Thus, according to the transformists, *change in behavior precedes change in structure* ... "form follows function."

With the Darwinists, the transformists believed that physical mutation must occur on a material base, localized but fundamentally concealed, in order for characteristics to be accumulated and passed on from one generation to the next. But whereas the former attributed the triggering of mutation to external, fortuitously accidental events, the latter suggested that such a base was nothing more or less than the niche of conversion where the organism received new directives from the psyche, along with a complex set of memories to be bequeathed to the next generation. All of this vital information had to be in some way imprinted (the "engram") and processed through a central nervous system, and it could only be verified by a change in behavior and/or appearance.

It was all a logical but empirically mysterious process. Today, biogeneticists seem on the brink of isolating the actual biochemical mechanism that will explain genetic transmutation. They may very well succeed. Yet as science has faithfully demonstrated, every milestone discovery is a Pandora's Box from which a flock of new questions also flies.

It should be borne in mind that neo-Lamarckism, being a *psychophysical* system, only lends itself part-way to reductive thinking. "Genetic memory" may indeed be grounded in specific mechanisms, but these probably constitute a system or series of systems of such intricacy that only the open-minded at the microscopes can rightfully appreciate it. The problem of transformism is that not enough of its backers have come from scientific ranks, due largely to the materialistic *Zeitgeist* that has so favored Darwinism. Even so, the microscope has paradoxically—if not always clearly—focused on the Lamarckian mystery of transmutational change and inheritance, in a sense helping to resurrect the evolutionist pariah who went to a pauper's grave.

Neo-Lamarckism cannot be offered up as a final version of evolution. It is not a perfect theory, if only because any theory must always be incomplete. As we have argued, however, it has substantially more to contribute in theory than Darwinism. And it is as good a foundation as we have in building a more serviceable theory. Bergson knew precisely where the neo-Darwinist currency failed and Lamarck's did not. In a tribute to that wondrous organ, the human eye, he capped the matter physiologically, leading off with the observation that any singular alteration of any component of the eye ("unless this change is infinitesimal") will produce impaired vision or blindness, while mutually coordinated, complementary changes are necessary for the ocular adjustments that continue or improve vision under complex conditions.[16]

After Butler and Bergson, the most well-known neo-Lamarckian is the brilliant writer and philosopher George Bernard Shaw. In many of his writings and plays, Shaw is a vocal critic of neo-Darwinism, while at the same time injecting support for his views on creative, transformative evolution, Shaw was a great admirer of Bergson, and his ideas on creative evolution and the Life Force predominate as themes in at least two of his plays, *Back to Methuselah* and *Man and Superman*. In *Man and Superman*, for example, speaking through the character of Don Juan, Shaw writes,

> Are we agreed that Life is a force which has made innumerable experiments in organizing itself; that the mammoth and the man, the mouse and the megatherium, the flies and the fleas and the Fathers of the Church, are all more or less successful attempts to build up that raw force into higher and higher individuals, the ideal individual being omnipotent, onmiscient, infallible, and withal completely unilludedly self-conscious: in short, a god?[17]

Shaw is alluding here to (in his interpretation) the prime aim of creative evolution—the striving in nature for self-awareness and self-knowledge.

Speaking through the character of Franklyn in *Back to Methuselah*, Shaw posits that all of scientific opinion, poetry, philosophy, and religion will eventually converge upon the central idea of creative evolution—that "it is going to be the religion that has its intellectual roots in philosophy and science just as medieval Christianity had its intellectual roots in Aristotle."[18]

Friedrich Nietzsche was also a supporter of the Lamarckian idea of the inheritance of acquired characteristics, as reflected in many of his works. For example, writing in 1886 (*Beyond Good and Evil*), he states that

> one cannot erase from the soul of a human being what his ancestors liked most to do and did most constantly: whether they were, for example, assiduous savers and appurtenances of desk and cash box, modest and bourgeois in their desires, modest also in their virtues. ... It is simply not possible that a human being should *not* have the qualities and preferences of his parents and ancestors in his body, whatever appearances may suggest to the contrary. This is the problem of race.[19]

After Shaw and Nietzsche, and other than the writings of H. Graham Cannon and the naturalist Joseph Wood Krutch, the transformative view of evolution has remained in abeyance, largely due to the wide-spread acceptance of Darwinism or of the neo-Darwinian "modern synthesis." As noted earlier, this was largely due to the impact of Darwin's carefully assembling the evidence for evolution, which in the process, right or wrong, also assured the impact of his theory. Darwinism also seemed to fit well with the ongoing *Zeitgeist* within technological society and reductionistic science. And the publicity his theories received in the original Scopes trial of 1925 also helped contribute to his widespread popularity.

The present-day interest in "whole mind" thinking, psychology, creativity, and human potential is producing (or is part of) a *Zeitgeist* that is beginning to move in a new direction. This *Zeitgeist* will undoubtedly be sympathetic to a Lamarckian conception of evolution, especially if scientific evidence can be cited to substantiate it. As earlier mentioned, the major obstacle to date for biologists has been the difficulty of neo-Lamarckians to shore up evidence supporting the existence of a mechanism(s) to account for the principle of the inheritance of acquired characteristics. Even though the Lamarckian system is in principle a more convincing explanation of evolution (and surely more acceptable to common sense) than is Darwinism, the identification of a physiological process or mechanism enabling the inheritance of acquired characteristics would be significant in allowing for wider scientific and public acceptance.

To conclude, Lamarck and Butler proposed the basis for an alternative theory of evolution—one which takes us far beyond the relatively restricted limits of the Darwinian view. The Lamarck-Butler psychophysical theory was not readily accepted for various reasons, as mentioned. We shall see in the next chapter, however, that scientific research has learned much over the past century to substantiate Lamarck; but it is scientific *thinking* that has failed to keep pace.

Chapter Ten

BIOLOGICAL TRANSMUTATION

Strictly speaking, all transforming processes can be called evolutionary. The development of a chicken from an egg, the development of an oak from an acorn, the development of wheat from a grain, the development of a butterfly from an egg, a caterpillar and a chrysalis; all these are examples of evolution actually existing in the world.

P. D. Ouspensky,
A New Model of the Universe

*The scientist has the vow and duty to hold his theory lightly, and to
depart with it joyously when it conflicts in any way with the facts.*

Thomas Henry Huxley,
"Darwin's Bulldog"

*Every man who has mastered a profession
is a skeptic concerning it.*

George Bernard Shaw

In T. H. Huxley's time the "Age of Information" had numerous decades
to go before being so obtusely dubbed. But it was well under way, and
perhaps it was an inkling of the invasion of facts to come that prompted
"Darwin's Bulldog" to make his admonishment. The master, Darwin
himself, freely acknowledged the problems with his theory, unlike
many 20th-century ideologues in and outside of science. A quite different breed of bulldog, they clamp into a theory so tenaciously that it is
too soon drained of its lifeblood.

In previous pages we touched upon the topic of the *Zeitgeist*, or
"time-spirit," which in the last two European centuries has been so
productive of things and facts and so destructive of mind and nature's
cohesion. In addition, the decreasing yield of reductionistic theory in
science was underscored by the parallel outgrowth of the materialistic
Zeitgeist. We saw in "neo-Darwinism" the attempt to hybridize into
productivity an idea fecund only in its first assumption: Humankind is
the apex of an ongoing process of organic change and development,
that is, evolution. Taking up the Darwinian extrapolations from there,
we pointed up their conceptual and evidential inadequacies, rooted in
reductionism.

As we approach the 21st century, we are witnessing and, in
greater or lesser degrees, effecting a change in our *Zeitgeist*. Religion,
art, and science are encountering each other anew and are melding a
new consciousness that will transcend all three, if the metaphysicians
are accurate prophets. They were certainly the first abstractionists of
evolution. Orthodox, literalist religion and positivistic, reductionistic
science have been the formal retardants to a truly eclectic *Zeitgeist*.
Lest we judge Darwin's followers for their mental rigidity too harshly,
however, we should note that they still appear avant-garde framed
against their conventional, die-hard opponents, the creationists who
are currently enjoying a revival. Creationism once again faces Darwinism in the courtroom, and the case's so-called facts are more anach-
ronistic now than they were when Clarence Darrow and William
Jennings Bryan marshalled their opposing arguments. "Scopes II"—as
this new flare-up of fundamentalism's attacks on evolution is called—
is as fine a specimen of cultural throwback as a historian could ask for.

Bound no less than its own subject matter to the very principles it seeks to reveal, evolutionary theory is in the throes of change. This is evidenced in part by the current resurgence of interest in the field. A transformist might say that the chrysalis of a new consciousness is struggling to emerge from its psychic cocoon. Whether the metamorphosis will result in a collectively advanced species of thought on the matter is open to question. We have broached the possibility of devolution of life forms, and nothing assures us that consciousness is yet an exception. On the contrary, with "creationism" and similar dogma we see a rehardening of the cocoon. One can only hope that the chrysalis will be able to break through its brittleness before irreversible damage is done.

On the experimental side, there is reason for encouragement. Research data is coming in so rapidly from the biological sciences that a mild form of fixation is required for the layman to keep up. Hypotheses are flying. What is under way now is much more than "Darwinist revisionism," as some establishmentarians have it. Rather, there are empirical schisms in the foundations of the orthodoxy, in need of replacement if a better structure is to be erected. Every experiment has encouraged heresy, be it nominally supportive of Darwinism or not.

This chapter will be a summary review of the pertinent research in biogenetics of the last two decades. Included will be some reflections on its import by a number of prominent cross-disciplinarians and authorities in the field. With this abundant, sometimes overwhelming, harvest of findings from the laboratory, the reader will realize that there are vast expanses of fallow soil in evolutionist theory, neglected by the Darwinist orthodoxy who have long overworked or misworked a few plots of hypothetical ground.

The "creationist" dogma can be laid to rest finally in the laboratory, not the courtroom. The deciding testimony will derive from empirically replicable phenomena, heretofore ususpected by traditional religionists and evolutionists alike. As we will see, the strength of the current biogenetic research is in its deep complexity—so much so, in fact, that the hypothesists are working overtime.

Although there are key mechanisms still to be found before a complete neo-Lamarckian model can be offered, data now available support the case for a highly ordered system of gene transmutation in plant, animal, and human species. Such is the basis for any scientifically credible transformationist theory.

Theodore Roszak has suggested a general context for genetic transmutation that so far fits the facts of inheritance studies. Life on earth, he reminds us, is a remarkable product of variability and flexibility. Geneticists have attributed the mutational plasticity of extant species to a high capacity for fortuitous error ("happy accident") in DNA coding.

But why continue to call "errors" those events that increasingly appear to be perpetuated by the needs and behavior of the organism? Absolute mutational invariance could conceivably have stabilized life at the stage of the protozoa, but there would also have been absolutely no potential for further development.

On the other hand, a total lack of invariance would result in form-destroying chaos. We are forced, as in physics, to think in relativistic terms, to seek a median principle. We know, for example, that the entity of "mind" in human beings is capable of tremendous powers of healing and creativity when balanced in this principle. When it breaks down, succumbs to extremes, pathology results. If all organisms are thus sustained and extinguished, we see the crucial need for nonfortuitous precision in the precarious DNA coding for passing acquired characteristics over generations. For it is in the continuity of these accumulated characteristics that survival depends, and any accidental mutation of the process would in all probability rigidify or debond the molecular structure of the coding system. The DNA transcription would be jammed or garbled. Roszak offers:

> Suppressing mutational error would almost seem to be the first order of evolutionary business—if indeed what we are dealing with here is "error," rather than the free play that unfolding potentiality requires.... How far fetched is it, then to imagine that organisms— or at least a strong-willed Few of them pioneering their way toward an interesting new environment or an inviting new behavior— might not, after some generations of trial and error, at least nudge their nucleic acids into the shape of a suitable mutation?[1]

Need, instinct, and memory ever "nudge" the organism toward experiment and complexity. The greater adventure of evolution is under way. Life wends its way by goal-oriented trial and error through the mazes of increasing consciousness, Roszak concludes, until

> there might finally emerge a human animal of rare sensitivity whose curiosity could sense the existence of environments no longer physical, where the adaptation required of all the species was a subtle change of consciousness.[2]

Roszak is speaking mainly in terms of human evolution. But again, at what level does consciousness—or more elementally, the capacity for the mutation option— begin? No one at this time can say. Let us hypothesize quite arbitrarily that it commences in a significant organic degree at the level of our protozoa, a successful population-stable species. In response to their internal and external needs and demands (i.e., survival and transcendence), the successful strains have obviously opted for more adaptive nonpathological behavior than their stagnant or extinct cousins. Thus, the resultant mutation is more of an effect than a cause of the process. The chosen behavior is the cause.

In the early 1960s a variety of research in genetics and molecular biology was the real springboard for the idea that gene mutation was controlled and perhaps initiated by systems within the organism. Findings strongly indicated that the brain and central nervous system (CNS), after interacting with the environment, modified and fed back DNA-RNA patterns to special target areas in the formative germ plasm inside the gonads. A "tagging hormone" acted as the biochemical bond for the restructured code. Charles Musés and Arthur M. Young presented the first formal deposition of the phenomenon.[3]

Further work later in the decade by John L. King and Thomas H. Jukes at the University of California at Berkeley revealed the existence of "Darwinianly neutral" mutations (i.e., independent of the censoring process of natural selection) that played a central part in evolving genetic codes by being transcribed into selected transfer RNA molecules.[4] The thesis of DNA modification by the brain (or CNS)—mediated by alterations in germ plasm—via modified RNA gained in respectability. "Natural selection" lost its Darwinist meaning in the scheme. Experiment verified what common sense had known all along: the brain (and simpler CNS analogues in lower animals) was the true innovator of change. Far from being a mere mechanical reactor to genetic accident, much data pointed to it as the initiator of mutation itself.

Brain physiologists have contributed much to our understanding of hormone regulation and gene biochemistry. The neural circuitries that integrate the boggling varieties of conscious and subconscious experience are just beginning to be mapped. Very few nonscientists appreciate the magnitudes involved. The enormously expanded rational power of the cerebral cortex in humans, for example, amazes the most seasoned experts. At the lower end (i.e., the limbic system) the most primitive motivations of behavior have yielded to no precise schematics. Holonomic (holistic) regulation and bilateral hemispherical specialization (e.g., analytical and intuitive modalities) are only semantical hints of the brain's boundless capacity.

Likewise, the intricacies of the gene are unsuspected by all but the most interested of the lay public. It will be recalled that the first model of the "atom of heredity" was the culmination of hybridization experiments on pea strains by Gregor Mendel in 1865. Although this conceptual prototype was useful as an introduction to the idea of such a mechanism, it was, through no fault of Mendel's, a gross simplification of the actual entity. Microscopy was a crude process by today's standards. Therefore, Mendel's conclusions fit easily, deceptively, into the simplistic Darwinian set, somewhat like a couple of random Chinese boxes misplaced from the whole sequence.

NON-MENDELIAN GENES

Darwinism has always been (and in a sense still is) based on a *static* Mendelian view of the gene. It views the gene as simply something passively resting in the cells (cell nuclei) of the body and reliably passing on identical hereditary information from one generation to the next. Modern research, however, reveals many exceptions to Mendelism (even though Mendelism holds in limited cases), and in fact, today, "non-Mendelian" genetics is more the rule, with Mendelian genetics the exception. Hence, most traits are controlled by sequences or multilevel systems of genes. Furthermore, research in the past decade reveals genes to be highly *dynamic*, many of them continually in action, monitoring and directing the various processes in the living body. For example, in a recent article titled "Genes That Move to Fight Disease," the research of molecular biologist Philip Leder of the National Institutes of Health illuminates the dynamic qualities of genes, especially as they function in conjunction with the immune system. It was discovered that three different classes of genes continually and mutually interact, actively combining and recombining to function in the production of antibodies to combat viruses.[5]

Another interesting set of studies is described in a paper titled "Genes That Violate Mendel's Rules," by James F. Crow. In this article, Crow describes various sorts of genes in various species that have been discovered to (in his words) "cheat" the conventionally known system of inheritance, thereby favoring their own survival and giving other genes an unequal disadvantage in the "gene shuffling" process resulting from sexual reproduction.[6]

More recent studies indicating the sophistication of organismic genetic systems (beyond anything that neo-Darwinism could ever accommodate) reveal several such curiosities: for example, "jumping genes," "bits of DNA" that "move about" along strands of chromosomes[7]; also "left-handed DNA," which is a kind of 'mirror image' form of the more familiar, right-handed DNA.[8] Both the jumping genes and left-handed DNA are thought to play an important role in the overall gene-regulation process.

It is now also suspected that genes by themselves do not *determine* anything; genes serve to *influence* the development and expression of traits, systems, and psychophysiological networks. This influence is greatly dependent upon the interaction of the genes with the internal and external environment or experiences to which they are continually exposed. Genes may be considered *inert* without appropriate environmental/experiential stimulation.

"CENTRAL DOGMA" VIOLATED

When Watson and Crick first discovered the DNA code in the early 1950s, they adopted a doctrinaire stance in the Darwinian mode. This was the Watson-Crick "central dogma" that posits: (1) that the DNA code is inviolable—it is stable and static, being impermeable to change unless altered by unusually noxious agents (*viz.*, "Darwinian" mutations); and (2) that the DNA code (or, nuclear DNA) is endowed with a certain *exclusiveness* in controlling inheritance.

To the chagrin of Darwinists (who rarely acknowledge it openly), several lines of research have fully discredited the central dogma since its inception in the 1950s.

Barry Commoner was the first to criticize the central dogma when, after reviewing fresh evidence, he boldly stated that inheritance is determined by DNA properties "only when DNA is a participating constituent of a living cell." Commoner stood on its head the modern Darwinian stricture that "DNA is the secret of life," holding instead that "life is the secret of DNA."[9]

Or, more genetically, DNA is a contributing propagational agent of larger living structures, not the static or sole lifegiver of those structures.

The "central dogma" is represented in the following descriptive formula:

$$\circlearrowleft DNA \longrightarrow RNA \longrightarrow Protein$$

This describes the self-duplicating nature of DNA and its alleged one-way effect upon RNA and the manufacture of protein. Unlike any other biochemical or physiological process in the cell or organism, however, this dogma does not allow for the frequently encountered principle of mutual feedback.

The first empirical exception to the dogma came in 1964, when Howard M. Temin revealed that the induction of cancer in animals by RNA viruses provided evidence that their RNA could modify the coding of the host DNA. He claimed to have found a stretch of host DNA that matched the nucleotide sequence on the RNA of the virus infecting the cells. These findings were later published in a paper in *Nature* with S. Mizutasi. Related discoveries independently cropped up at about the same time, including the work of Sol Spiegelman at Columbia and D. Baltimore at M.I.T. Spiegelman, for example, found in six different tumor-inducing RNA viruses an enzyme that could synthesize DNA on RNA templates. Other papers promptly appeared, and the reality of this *reverse transcriptase enzyme*, as it was named, was established.

During 1971 and 1972 high levels of reverse transcriptase enzymes were discovered in the white blood cells of leukemia patients and in malignant tumor tissues, but not in corresponding cells. Later (1972), in an article titled "RNA-Directed DNA Synthesis," Temin provided evidence to suggest that, in addition to RNA-directed DNA synthesis in the formation of cancer, it is quite likely that this same process occurs in the normal state of affairs.[10]

With RNA providing the template, DNA could be changed into something different. This RNA-directed process would allow for the "amplification" of DNA, and Temin also suggests that this may be a key factor in the embryologic differentiation of cells. It is noteworthy that these are the ideas of a contemporary scientist who, consciously or otherwise, is advocating something suggestive of a rudimentary mechanism allowing for the inheritance of acquired characteristics—that quaint Lamarckian idea.

With the "central dogma" now in question, the new descriptive formula would appear as follows:

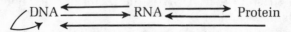

A second exception to the Watson-Crick dogma has been found in subsequent research revealing quite clearly that, in addition to DNA control, "extra-chromosomal" factors often play a role in heredity: that is, agents in the cytoplasm of the cell are involved besides those situated in the nucleus. An example is the work of Sir Cyril Hinshelwood (and others) on microlical systems. Another example comes from Professor Roger Williams at the University of Texas; he undertook several studies involving the interbreeding of rats and mice, which suggested extra-chromosomal contributions to differences between these animals.[11]

However, these earlier studies with rodents had failings that could open them to criticism. There was still no means of obtaining hard evidence—at least not until that unusual character called the "nine-banded armadillo" stepped onto the laboratory stage. Whenever a single reproductive cell is fertilized in this species, the cell divides into four embryos to yield identical quadruplets at birth. But it was not until comparisons of organ weights and biochemical factors were made that differences were found in these supposedly identical quads. Twenty parameters were measured in sixteen sets of quads, and up to 140 trait variations were recorded in a single set. Typically, though the nuclei of the four embryos are fair visual replicas of one another, the organelles (i.e., minute structures, such as ribosomes, mitochondria, etc.) in the outer cytoplasm are unequally divided and their complex factors account for the very real variations between the quads.[12]

This discovery encouraged researchers to begin focusing in on the cell cytoplasm. Slowly it was found that interesting things were happening there in terms of hidden genetics. By the turn of this decade a number of cytoplasmic investigators realized that the Watson-Crick gene-monopoly could be broken. Among these were biologists Carl Lindegren and Lynn Margulis, who furthered the heresy of "cytoplasmic heredity" by elaborating its basic symbiotic principle. In Greek, *symbiosis* means "life together." The cytoplasm, these theorists held, is a hitherto unsuspected site for symbiotic mutualism. The evolution of complex plant and animal species had proceeded via bacterial symbiosis. In an intriguing article titled "Dogma and Iconoclasm in Biology: The Gene Is Not Enough," Lindegren and Margulis clarified that the cytoplasmic dynamics of each nucleated cell are not insulated from that of others but, on the contrary, are integrated in functional associations ("communities"). This is extrapolated from the fact that all plant and animal cells are "the products of symbiosis between bacteria and the so-called cytoplasmic (outside the nucleus) hereditary systems of the original bacteria symbiants."

These scientists go on to emphasize that mutational change in the nucleotide base sequences of chromosomal DNA seems by itself an inadequate triggering mechanism for the structural leaps and bounds of evolutionary innovation. Though natural selection draws its raw material from the mutations of single cells, this does not supply what is needed for the work of actual morphological transmutation. State Lindegren and Margulis, "Symbiotic partnerships have been crucial for the origin of many new organs and organisms."[13]

Lindegren and Margulis go on to explain that symbiosis is a kind of "parasexuality" that, ancient and pervasive, innovates sexuality as a facilatory mode of propagation. Parasexuality is the coming together of the members of different species for "fertilization" and propagation of each. Leguminous plants and their nitrogen-fixing bacteria are examples of this symbiosis. Later they may separate, the plant to produce seeds, the bacteria to reenrich the soil. The process is in principle not so different from that of meiosis after egg-sperm fertilization in sex. Union is followed by separation after propagation, then reunion in completion. In the former it is in the nitrogen-fixing mature plant, in the latter a new bond by offspring. Both involve fusion, and in the highly evolved organisms we see their marvelous complementation. Thus, "cytoplasmic heredity" should not be thought such a radical concept.

As nucleic mutation alone—even a vitalized version—cannot account for the overall flexibility of the organism, as demanded by evolutionary contingencies, it was logical for biogeneticists to begin searching seriously for a second genetic system in the cytoplasm. Such a one had already been isolated by Ruth Sager at Columbia University as early as 1965. "Nonchromosomal genes" were, however, given small credence as important hereditary factors by establishment geneticists. They persisted in viewing the cytoplasm as little more than a support system for the cell nucleus.

On the other hand, Sager's analysis indicated that non-chromosomal genes were biochemically distinct structures composed, like DNA, of nucleic acids, though they did not conform to standard genetic analysis. She further speculated that the cytoplasm possibly contained other complete genetic systems not based on DNA, concluding that organelle growth may have an ongoing dependence upon nonchromosomal genetic systems for the flexibility required by its variable environment.[14]

GENE REGULATION

In 1983, corn geneticist Barbara McClintock received the Nobel Prize, as well as a $60,000-a-year lifetime grant from Chicago's MacArthur Foundation, for her research on maize, beginning in the 1940s, which revealed that genetic structures were not stable or immutable (much to the astonishment of establishmentarian "wisdom"); her studies disclosed that the pigment genes that cause the splotches of color on maize kernels were in some way being switched on and off by certain mysterious "controlling elements." It was thought that possibly the genes were normally in an "off" or repressed state and that the controlling agents acted to turn them "on" by derepression (this later became known as the "derepressor hypothesis").

This preliminary research fully dispelled the notion that genes operated along a one-way street, directing traffic without modification. It is now well established that genes themselves are continually controlled by other agents. What exists, in fact, is a two-way thoroughfare with intersections and interchanges in which traffic moves according to the laws of give-and-take typical of all organismic processes (and the entire universe as well)—that is, feedback.

Genes seem to be regulated largely by hormone flows, though precisely how and how much remain a puzzle. Research has shown that these specialized secretions play a leading role in the operator/repressor function governing genetic processes. Steroid hormones, for example, appear to do this in an intimate, but indirect way by first acting upon a mediating agent—specific protein receptor molecules adjacent to the DNA. These receptors in turn influence the expression of genes via other mediating protein agents—histones and nonhistones

(histones tend to keep genes turned off, while nonhistones selectively turn them on).[15]

The feedback system, now known as the DNA operator-repressor system, is based on two facts: (1) adjacent to every gene is a segment of DNA called an operator, and (2) this operator is primarily under the control of proteins referred to as repressors that bind to the operator to influence the expression of the gene.

In an article titled "A DNA-Repressor System," Tom Marriates and Mark Ptashne—after reviewing their ambitious studies on the virus, as well as the effect of enzymes (specifically RNA-polymerase) and proteins upon genetic function—forecast that future research will reveal the DNA-repressor system to play a yet more complex, expanded role in gene regulation. The feedback dynamics between protein and DNA in this process are already yielding more specific secrets.[16]

Embryonic development also proceeds on interactions with the DNA code. Ever in flux, the code is akin to a complete lingual system, which nonetheless must be translated into numerous regional (organic) dialects before its messages can be received and acted upon. Perhaps a better analogy, one offered by Peter Beaconsfield, George Birdwood, and Rebecca Beaconsfield, is that of the endocrine "orchestra" that plays during pregnancy. In the early stages shortly after fertilization, the trophoblast and then the placenta produce hormones that are the functional analogues of the ones to be later manufactured by the pituitary gland of the developing fetus. These precursors orchestrate all functions vital to the fetus, until it is able to begin performing on its own. The activities are regulated indirectly, mainly by protein hormones acting upon steroid ones. The "score" is composed and delivered by DNA, but the music is actually made by the placenta itself and its hormone players. The steroids mediate between the placenta and pituitary protein hormones, conducting the genetic performance.[17]

HORMONES AND BEHAVIOR

Conclusively, then, genes and DNA exercise control and maintenance of the organism but are obedient themselves to feedback principles. Extranuclear and extracellular agents, primarily proteins and hormones, hold this mandate over the gene in reproductive and other functions.

Hormones also play important, if subtle, roles in interacting with neural mechanisms (and hence experience and behavior). Sex hormones are now known to pattern brain circuitry in newborn animals and influence later behavior. The gonads and adrenal cortex secrete steroids destined for special receptor cells in the brain.[18]

The hormonal relationship between the brain and endocrine glands has perhaps the most hidden ramifications for behavior, and its intricacies have proven to be among the most difficult for everyone in the field. But much has been learned. The neural system is another maze that seems to grow more perplexing the more it is mapped. Key "neurohormones" have been isolated, but they are as mere intimations of more intricate chemical-neurologic networks.

Certain "releasing factors," originating in the brain (i.e., the hypothalamus), regulate the activity of the anterior pituitary gland. This dynamic gland in turn controls the peripheral endocrine glands. Both the anterior and posterior lobes of the pituitary effect metabolic changes in the hypothalamus, but the latter reciprocates by regulating hormone output in the anterior pituitary, by way of certain hybrid neurohormones. Since the pituitary regulates a variety of functions in all the endocrine glands of the body, the effect of this hypothalamus-pituitary feedback system is therefore of utmost consequence. Various other biochemicals in the body also influence the hypothalamus, such as "neurotransmitters," which are chemicals released from the nerve-fiber endings that act as messengers for the nerve cells. "Noradrenaline" is a major neurotransmitter affecting the hypothalamus and, thereby, hunger, thirst, blood pressure, temperature regulation, behavior, and reproduction. Mood elevation and depression can be triggered by manipulation of noradrenaline volume in the brain.[19]

From these hard-won findings we can see that the hypothalamus is rather like a biochemical dispatcher of the brain, taking in and sending out directives. It is an integrator of primal functions within that ancient complex of structures we call the "limbic system." From this region derives all physical drives involving pleasure and pain, including their memory and anticipation. Thus it is an emotional center as well as a physical one and, consequently, it is the most powerful seat of behavior. It motivates far beyond the simple impulses of the lower centers (brain stem, cerebellum, etc.) while at the same time making contact with the higher centers (i.e., the cerebral cortex). The role of the limbic system is better appreciated when we realize that there is a continuous interaction in our minds between what we know or think and what we feel.

The intricate interaction between the limbic and genetic systems via hormonal mediation further suggests a linkage to a Lamarckian "mind-body" mechanism of evolution.

BIOCHEMISTRY OF MEMORY

As you are now more apt to appreciate, science has come a long way in the past several decades in intimating the possible physiological mechanisms underlying the inheritance of acquired characteristics. It is well established that inheritance is controlled by cytoplasmic factors as well as nuclear DNA and that the latter is often regulated by external agents, such as proteins and hormones. In addition, hormones and brain structures closely interact, and experiences and behavior have an effect upon these brain structures.

There is, further, a reverse feedback in which the brain activates a hormone chain to the endocrine glands (i.e., pituitary), with these hormones regulating gene expression through proteins. And, just as genes operate to develop and maintain organismic processes, so the genes are equally responsive to conditions integral in the organism itself, and ultimately to its behavior and experience. The next logical question is: How do behavior and experience (via the CNS) serve to influence the genome and other structures related to heredity?

Conditioning and learning, or that which is "acquired" in Lamarckian terms, depends ultimately upon memory. Memory can be divided into three types along a time dimension: short-term, medium-range, and long-term memory. Neurophysiologically, studies presently suggest that memory generally holds to these basic criteria: (1) *short-term memory* primarily involves neurologic functioning (circuitry dynamics), (2) *medium-range memory* entails a combination of circuitry dynamics and macromolecular (biochemical) processes, and (3) *long-term memory* is seen as primarily macromolecular.

For the sake of parsimony, neuroscientists most often prefer to divide memory simply into a long and a short form. For short-term memory, the most commonly accepted model bases itself upon the electroencephalogram (EEG), which reveals the brain to be in ceaseless electrical activity. The theory here is that the memory trace takes "the form of a circuit of continuously self-exciting neurons.... As few as two or three neurons could form a nerve net, and around this net a continuously reverberating circuit of current could flow. As each neuron could take part, by way of its synaptic connections, in many such nets the coding potential of the 10^{10} neurons of the cortex would be ample for the memories."[20]

Because the EEG is so labile, and because the electrical activity of the brain is easily distorted or temporarily abolished by such things as drugs, body cooling, and so forth, longer-term memory demands another explanatory model. Such a model must be built upon a more or less quantitative change in some biochemical property of the cells. A compositional shift of substances must occur if there is to be an enduring neurologic record. Only then can the memory store be stabilized beyond short-term.

Here again research supports a "radical" idea. In repeated experiments RNA and protein levels are shown to increase in response to the exertions of structured learning. Emotion, stress, and random activity produce marked changes in biochemistry, but these are quite unlike that of RNA-protein production during the cerebral calibrations of purposeful learning. Conversely, emotional stress seems to deplete protein reserves.

Added support for these findings demonstrating a connection between learning/conditioning and RNA-protein buildup comes from the fact that protein synthesizes very rapidly in the brain and, further, that a greater percentage of brain DNA is "turned on" and involved in its own synthesis than in any other organ in the body.

To continue, in addition to studies that have detected enhanced protein and RNA production in response to learning experience, another series of studies has proven to be even more interesting. Psychophysiologist James McConnell and associates trained flatworms to learn a maze and then had these flatworms chopped up and fed to "naive" flatworms; they discovered that the naive flatworms were no longer so—they now knew how to *solve* the maze. Later, McConnell (as well as others) was able to extract RNA from trained rats and hamsters and reinject the RNA into naive rats, with the same results.

The researcher Holger Hydén reviews studies in this area, and especially his own extensive series of investigations—substantiating the participation of RNA, proteins, and DNA in the operation of memory. He speculates that the reticence of Darwinian behavioral geneticists in the wake of this evidence for the necessity of RNA-protein synthesis in brain cells for long-term memory is due to the obvious Lamarckian implications.[21]

Nonetheless, after several decades of research in this area, Hydén does appear to support a revised view of Lamarckian evolution. He hypothesizes that enough variations (e.g., 10,000) in nucleotide sequence could result in an "evolutionary event," the possibility arising from the production of a wide variety of surface proteins (necessary for intercellular exchange) by the repeated sequences of such gene sets. He suggests that this protein enrichment, the mechanism of memory storage, results in new learning and experience, which in turn initiates additional differentiation of brain cells. Environmental input stimulates further activity in the quiet areas of the genome, synthesizing scores of slightly variant RNA strains and proteins. According to Hydén, these intricate genetic processes are the effects of "the productions of a change in ionic equilibrium through field changes." On the nuclear level, conformational changes are effected by the field changes via activating proteins giving rise to RNA synthesis (from new gene areas). Adds Hydén, "Even instructional changes could occur."[22]

The process mentioned by Hydén concurrently occurs by way of an orchestration of repression and derepression of genetic material (DNA, RNA). It is during learning periods, when neurons make contact, that RNA variations take place, with research indicating that the mechanism is triggered by derepression of genetic stimulation.[23] This is the familiar derepressor hypothesis, invoked within the context of memory. The full idea is nicely summarized in a schematism provided by E. Roy John in his comprehensive book, *Mechanisms of Memory*.[24]

> Thus, we propose the following scheme, which we call the *Derepressor Hypothesis*:
>
> (A) In any cell, much of the potential for synthesis of specific substances inherent in the DNA structure is repressed.
>
> (B) Sustained participation of a neuron in representational activity causes a shift in the concentration of cytoplasmic materials, resulting in the derepression of an inhibited synthesis.
>
> (C) The resulting alteration in cytoplasmic constituents has two consequences:
>
> > (1) Derepression of that synthesis is thereafter sustained.
>
> > (2) The reactivity of the neuron to patterns of stimulation is altered.
>
> This scheme is illustrated in detail [below]. Thus the feedback loop becomes self-sustaining and changed neural reactivity (step 11) is postulated to be a byproduct of this loop.

$$4 \leftarrow 10$$
$$\uparrow \qquad \downarrow$$
$$5 \qquad 9$$
$$\uparrow \qquad \downarrow$$
$$6 \qquad 8$$
$$\nwarrow \; \nearrow$$
$$7$$

In a most mazelike way, this tedious biogenetic tracking leads to further proof of an intricate feedback system between the genome ("the sum of the entire genetic makeup of the organism") and the organismic milieu outside of it. (See the full schematic on the next page.)

The idea of a "master-gene," or master system, has become accepted as necessary by some geneticists. There must be some kind of holistic monitoring mechanism for the genome, which this term describes. All cells carry identical genetic information, yet each cell belongs to a larger system of specialized cells. Somehow genetic information is selectively turned "on" or "off" to determine the specialization of a cell (e.g., liver cells, heart cells, brain cells, etc.). The recent discovery by Walter J. Gehring of the University of Basel of a short stretch of DNA called the homeobox provides the first empirical support for such a control system (or a rudimentary form of it). Possibly the master-gene system holonomically monitors the effects of lifelong

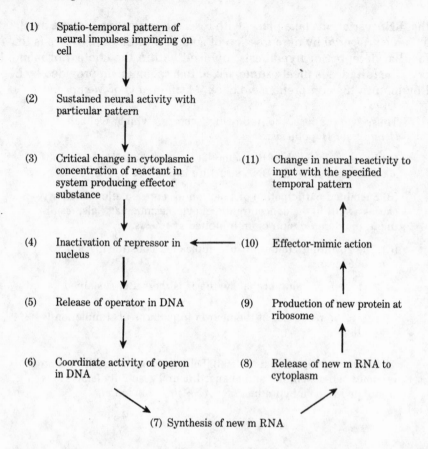

(1) Spatio-temporal pattern of neural impulses impinging on cell

(2) Sustained neural activity with particular pattern

(3) Critical change in cytoplasmic concentration of reactant in system producing effector substance

(11) Change in neural reactivity to input with the specified temporal pattern

(4) Inactivation of repressor in nucleus ←——— (10) Effector-mimic action

(5) Release of operator in DNA

(9) Production of new protein at ribosome

(6) Coordinate activity of operon in DNA

(8) Release of new m RNA to cytoplasm

(7) Synthesis of new m RNA

experience, conditioning, and learning, these patterns of information being impressed upon the genes themselves (via DNA/RNA activity). These general patterns could then be registered within the "memory" of the master system, with the possibility of transmission to offspring. The operation of the master system might be analogous to that of the modern computer that is capable of quickly processing great amounts of information input, analyzing the data, and yielding a readout showing trends, macropatterns, even forecasts derived by extrapolation.

Memory is also apparently involved in immunologic functioning, in which antibodies "learn" to recognize antigens with increasing efficiency over time. It is no surprise then that proteins and DNA/RNA processes have been linked to immunologic memory; whereas DNA and RNA molecules provide the dynamics for genetic memory, protein grinds the gears for the immunologic mode. All three (DNA, RNA, protein) are collectively known as "informational macromolecules," since they are able to arrange a precise information-code by sequencing their subunits (nucleotide bases in DNA/RNA and amino acids in proteins).

In an article recently published in the British journal *Nature*— portentously titled "Simultaneous Yet Independent Inheritance of Somatically Acquired Tolerance of Two Distinct U-2 Antigenic Haplotype Determinants in Mice"—R. B. Gorcynski and E. J. Steele caused quite a stir when they reported the results of their research (along with prior studies by the same and other researchers) indicating support for a Lamarckian hypothesis "predicting soma to germ-line inheritance for acquired states of the immune system" and concluding that the results are an "even stronger reason for abandoning the notion of the isolation of the germ line from the soma (Weismann's doctrine)."[25] Basically Gorcynski and Steele, in an experiment with four mice at the Ontario Cancer Institute, began by eliminating the mice's natural tendency to reject skin grafts from other mice. The four mice then sired 150 offspring, with about half inheriting this tolerance. Many of these second-generation mice, in turn, passed this tolerance on to their own offspring.

Another genetic heresy stems from the discovery of "anti-antibodies." These somewhat inscrutable entities are extragenetic components, called "plasmids," that resist antibody effects. Plasmids are subunits within the cell whose chemical fluxions seem to anticipate life itself. Plasmids are exceptional examples of evolution through specific necessity. Their discovery came about only because Darwinian (mutational) factors could not satisfactorily account for antibody resistance. The precision of plasmids in countering antibodies is the result of long ages of functional refinement. Richard P. Novick, whose work helped isolate the factor, calls this refinement "exquisitely specific" and attributes it to necessitous learning. He centers his subsequent speculation on the question of how many different plasmids are able to independently establish a "specific structural interaction" with the host cell. He ventures the explanation that "each plasmid may have 'learned' to attach itself to a different structure in the cell ... by evolving a protein that binds to a specific site." Novick believes that many unknown factors of this molecular symbiosis will be uncovered by future research.[26]

Once again, a Lamarckian idea is reinforced. A number of neo-Darwinists, however, are now attempting to hold their ground by absorbing the spearheads of the new research. Subversive references to "learning" and "memory" are therefore cropping up sporadically in their writings. Some have even conceded that organismic memory is a function of mathematical sequences in the genetic code over generations. Manfred Eigen, William Gardiner, Peter Schuster, and Ruthild

Winkler-Opwatitsch are a team of neo-Darwinian geneticists who claim that computer analysis supports the case for "ancestral information." They cite work of John Shepherd, at the University of Basel, who has studied the incidence of sequential repetition of code characters of DNA viruses, bacteria genes, and higher organisms. Shepherd concluded that the new genes retain a memory of their ancestral sequences, the triplet RNY being the forerunner of RNA. "Ancestral information can be distinguished from later modifications" is the modest concurrence of these Darwinists.[27]

When one theoretical camp begins borrowing bits and pieces of another's terminology, we can be sure that an eclectic shift is under way. We can also be sure that in this case it is the neo-Darwinists who are doing most of the shifting. And they still have a good amount to do. For if learning and memory are indeed motivators of evolution, what is it, if not the organism itself, that is doing the learning and remembering? The definition of "memory" in *Webster's New World Dictionary* is a Lamarckian one: "the ability or power of retaining or reviving in the mind past thoughts, images, ideas, etc."

If *mind* is admitted to the issue, a basic axiom of Darwinism is negated, this being its assumption that the organism (or its constituent parts) does not perpetuate the progress of its own evolution, and that it (its progress) is totally fortuitous.

Time itself is subverting Darwinian dogma as the expertise continues to pile up. Theory can be supported by the most solid and broad pillars of hypothesis as the empirical ground shifts. Transmutation provides a strongly girded framework for an evolutionary theory. Random mutation, by contrast, cannot even lay a clinical cornerstone. No amount of statistical or other sophistications will enable it to do so. "Genetic drift," "mutant distributions," and "quasispecies" are anemic abstractions beside the less clinical but more experiential concretions of habit, memory, motivation, and so forth. Conditioning and learning are conceptually faceted to these terms in the most basic way.

So, semantically speaking, *transformation* and *transmutation* are validated by the depth and breadth of their common usage, and are even much more sensible to the familiar experience.

CYCLIC AMP

At another but related level of analysis are the recent investigations of "second messengers" in the brain.

In most organisms there are two main pathways of intercellular communication: the nervous system and the endocrine system. In the nervous system, nerve cells (neurons) conduct information from one to another by secreting neurotransmitter substances, these substances altering the electrical activity of the cells they affect. In the endocrine system, information is conducted from one area to another via the bloodstream, these messages being carried by hormones. According to James A. Nathanson and Paul Greengard in a paper titled "Second Messengers in the Brain," the molecular *modus operandi* of these two systems are principally the same: "In both systems, messenger molecules are released from one cell, travel a certain distance and interact with the surface of a second cell to modify its activity." The authors suggest that, since nature tends to favor economy and will repeat the simplest dynamic when it is successful, the mechanisms of various hormonal effects within an organism might be quite similar to those involved in the chemistry of neural transmission.[28] The chemicals that mediate these functions are referred to as "second messengers" (one of the class of small molecules known as nucleotides).

In the endocrine system, the "first messenger" in this relay network is the hormone which binds to the receptor (in the cell membrane). The second messenger is needed to carry the code on into the cell's inner biochemical machinery so that the low-level signal of the hormone can be amplified thousands of times. Cyclical AMP (adenosine monophosphate), generated by the enzyme adenylate cyclase, is this amplifying ("second") messenger. It is a derivative of adenosine triphosphate (ATP), the universal currency of cellular energy.

Having isolated this mechanism, Nathanson and Greengard then asked, "Can a similar mechanism help to explain how nerve cells communicate?" Yes, was the eventual answer. With investigative help from other researchers, they discovered that cyclic AMP also mediates information transfer from neuron to neuron. Certain neurotransmitters, by binding to a specific receptor, stimulate the production of cyclic AMP inside the receiving cell, with an increase in the level of cyclic AMP functioning to translate the message of the neurotransmitter into physiological action. The latter process is made possible by an interaction between cyclic AMP and the ions that serve to alter cell membrane permeability in neurotransmission.

As Nathanson and Greengard point out, this biochemical chain-of-command is modulatory and long-lasting in function, rather than initiatory. Any complex neural process that involves recurrent, intricate interactions tends generally to increase in permanency. The neuronal events sketched above seem to be a prime example.

The authors cite studies indicating that cyclic AMP-mediated synapses produce changes in membrane excitability lasting very long on the scale of neural events (from hundreds of milliseconds or longer— sometimes several hours) and conclude that this kind of evidence increases the likelihood that more permanent changes in the central nervous system are fundamentally originated by the mediation of cyclic nucleotides in synaptic events.[29]

Nathanson and Greengard continue with certain findings and ideas that directly bear upon the claim that nervous system activity (i.e., learned experience), as mediated by cyclic nucleotides, can have a direct effect upon the genome. These include research results pointing to the probability that activity within the cell nucleus is influenced by the phosphorylation of protein, as mediated by cyclic AMP. The latter, a product of synaptic activity, theoretically could indirectly expell phosphorylate histone (or a similar regulatory protein in the nucleus) by activating a protein kinase. The chemical gateway would consequently be open for messenger RNA transcription and, finally, codification for protein.[30]

The authors then suggest that cyclic AMP is an important link in the establishment of long-term memory and that such processes could constitute a molecular basis for information storage in the nervous system and, ultimately, the genome. They conclude that the synaptic and nonsynaptic activity of cyclic AMP should be looked upon as mutually reinforcing functions, parts of a larger integrated system that strongly impacts the genetic material in the cell nucleus, resulting in long-term changes in memory and subtle physiological processes.[31]

This is not mere speculation. Recent research is now establishing a link between cyclic AMP processes and conditioning/learning functions in simple animals. And the relevance of these processes in humans is apparent. In summarizing his own findings (using lower organisms) with cyclic AMP, researcher Eric R. Kandel concludes that, aside from advanced forms of mental activity (abstraction, reflection, analytical reasoning, etc.) found in humans and perhaps to some degree in higher primates, the basic conditioning processes that profoundly influence the brain and behavior (including humans) can oftentimes be produced by a relatively small network of neurons.[32]

Herein lies a physiological basis or mechanism involved in the genetic storage of information brought on by hormonal-neural activity in the organism. This "mechanism," along with other biochemical-bioelectrical agents and processes, assists in the establishment of long-term memories—storing these memories in genetic material—thereby enhancing the potential for eventual transmission of such information (as "transmuted genes") to future generations. The notion of genes as repositories for "extra-long-term" memory storage is apt.*

---

*See Annotation, "Microcomputers and Memory."

GAMETES AND THE REPRODUCTIVE SYSTEM

Spermatozoa and eggs divisibly contain the same genetic information as found in every other cell throughout the body. And the reproductive systems of males or females need not (as Weismann and others have erroneously implied) be considered different any more than any other organ system of the body may be considered different. All organ systems of the body are interrelated. The separate systems are only "different" in the sense that they each perform specialized functions; these specialized functions are meaningless unless considered a part of the whole.

Human reproduction is the product of numerous processes involving the coordinated dynamics of several organ systems in the body, especially the brain and endocrine system. In a revealing diagram (see the next page) neurobiologist Sheldon J. Segal shows how the brain and endocrine system interact in influencing the reproductive system.[33]

Note that Segal, in his description of the diagram, alludes to several of the mechanisms already discussed above (such a second messengers, hormone-gene derepression, etc.), indicating how they play a key role in the interaction of the brain and reproductive organs. The diagram also makes it much easier to grasp how Lamarck's "inheritance of acquired characteristics" might come about, Dr. Weismann notwithstanding.

Reproductive behavior is the result of the complex, coordinated interplay of several factors, including environmental conditions, hormones of the endocrine system and of the brain, and behavior. In a wide range of studies of animals (including mammals), it has been verified that the anterior hypothalamic-preoptic area of the brain operates as a major center for the integration of reproductive activity and behavior. Most interesting is the role played by the two sexes in mutually affecting one another, thereby stimulating activity in the integrative brain center, and hence in affecting activity within the reproductive system itself. Secondary sex characteristics (i.e., anatomical features) play a key stimulatory role, and the distinct behavior of either sex also has its effects. The *perception* by either sex of the opposite sex's anatomical features and each other's courtship behavior triggers hormones within the brain that in turn affect endocrine glands throughout the body and, especially, the gonads. Verified in several studies, this has been nicely reviewed in an article by researcher David Crews.[34] Crews also discovered an interesting relationship between male aggression and female physiology, namely that the former inhibits

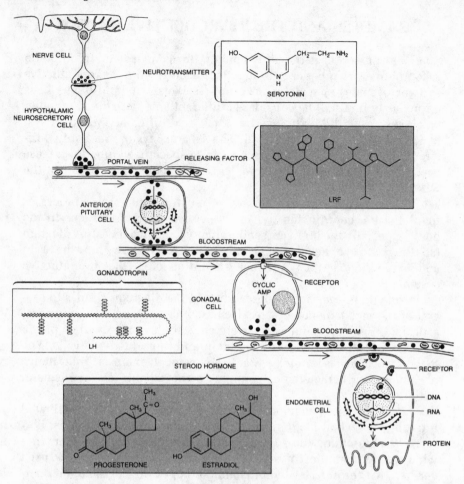

MOLECULAR RELAY that interrelates the reproductive organs is shown in more detail. A neurotransmitter (perhaps serotonin) is released from a specialized brain cell and excites a neurosecretory cell in the hypothalamus. The hypothalamic cell secretes a gonadotropin-releasing factor, the polypeptide LRF, into short portal veins that supply cells in the anterior pituitary and cause them to release their gonadotropins. These are large glycoproteins (whose structure is merely suggested here) that enter the general circulation. On reaching a specialized gonadal cell each of the gonadotropins acts, by way of the cyclic adenosine monophosphate "second messenger" system, to stimulate the synthesis of a specific steroid hormone; the two major female hormones are diagrammed. The gonadal steroids move through the bloodstream to reproductive-organ target cells, where they bind to receptors that carry them into the nucleus. There they either activate or "depress" genes to make new proteins and thus affect the organ's structure or function.

ovarian production in females. Crews maintains that this finding is a first in showing that female fertility can be dampered as well as activated by manipulation of the social-behavioral environment.[35]

Crews' observation is on target. Among other things, he suggests that male-female psychology—that is, their behavior, experiences, and, in humans, their conditioning patterns and thinking—plays an important role in stimulating or repressing the reproductive system. Since the regulation of the reproductive system is ultimately under control of hormones and of their subsequent effect upon the genetic substrate of cells within the gonads, again we see intimations of how a Lamarckian "psyche-soma" mechanism might operate.

We should keep in mind that the development of the two genders is a significant step in the evolution of higher organisms. Although Darwinians simply account for the evolution from asexual to sexual reproduction as just another "avenue" allowing for greater genetic variability, thus facilitating natural selection, the evidence demonstrates that there is much more to be made of this phenomenon. The development of two separate sexes opens up broad possibilities in the psychological variability of organisms. The interaction between the sexes plays a major role in affecting a significant proportion of our overall behavior (e.g., courting/dating, mating, family life, etc.) as well as our attitudes and thinking patterns. Conditioning also plays an ongoing role, and the continued evolution of the species may in some way depend upon this subtle male-female interactive phenomenon.

In considering the higher reaches of evolution (elaborated upon later on in this book), love appears to catalyze key elements, and unquestionably humans learn much of what they know about love in their intimate interactions with the opposite sex, from their parents or mates. The interactions between the sexes and what is learned there can thus provide essential preparation for attainment at a much higher experiential/evolutionary level.

Love, in both its most common and sublime forms, is the manifest transformation of lower, compulsive energies (sexual, territorial, group-preservative, etc.) into higher impulses that, for the most part, seem to have no connection to *immediate* physical survival. The hallmark of authentic sexual love is the general extravagance of its energy (à la Romeo and Juliet), far beyond what is needed for the simple perpetuation of biological life. In everyday circumstances this surplus is channeled into either negative or positive experiences that, depending on the emotional pole, will be destructive and counterevolutionary or creative and consciousness-raising. For the prodigies of energy required for the latter purpose, nature seems to have invented the unprecedented psychophysical alchemy of sex and love.[36]

Returning to the research, the general conclusion is that many of the mechanisms and processes that are thought to affect evolution by way of the inheritance of acquired characteristics are also operative within the reproductive system, which ultimately is responsible for assisting in the transmission of "information" from parents to offspring.

The evidence stands on its own, and the merits of the Lamarck-Butler position can now be better judged in this light. And even as you read this, research ceaselessly continues that will deepen our understanding of the complex mechanisms of evolutionary phenomena.

In review, evolution as a phenomenon is well established, scientifically and otherwise. Darwinism as a *theory* of evolution (and all its modern theoretical revisions and developments) is inaccurate or misplaced; it is above all a theory of species preservation (survival, adaptation, reproductivity, etc.) while the Lamarckian theory appears to be one of evolution *per se*. Evolution can be seen as a universal phenomenon and devolution as its universal, retarding phenomenon. Lamarckian theory can also be extended beyond the conventional limits of plant, animal, and human life; a series of "new" assumptions (Butler and Bergson) tends to extend the phenomenon of evolution to every form of matter. But if we, for the time being, restrict our view to conventional forms of life, contemporary research appears to substantiate the neo-Lamarckian view. This is largely possible by attempting to establish feasible physiological mechanisms underlying the key principle of the inheritance of acquired characteristics. This in turn has been accomplished by revealing how psychological processes act through the central and autonomic nervous system, influencing the endocrine system (and vice versa) and ultimately the genetic substrate.

All of the research cited herein (as well as new and accumulating research) tends to converge on common ground. The "mechanism" allowing for genetic transmutation and its transmission to offspring seems to involve the interplay of several psychophysiological factors. Physiological components that appear most important in the process include neurotransmitters, hormones, cyclic AMP, reverse transcriptase enzymes (RNA-directed DNA synthesis), and protein. Transmutation of DNA may take place via RNA-directed synthesis and/or derepression patterning, this in turn under control by hormones and cyclic AMP. Hormones and cyclic AMP are key agents that respond to many forms of brain activity, and certainly to those activities that involve emotion, drive, pleasure, pain, learning, and memory. Whereas recurring learning experiences tend to be stored as long-term memory—in encoded form in RNA/protein inside brain cells—this information (via RNA-directed synthesis) is carried into DNA, whereupon it is stored as "extra-long-term" memory in genes. Although not commonly described this way but easily understood within this context, the essence of the gene is its storage capability for "extra-long-term memory" in encoded informational form. Through a process of holonomic-systemic influence (from brain to body to gonadal cells), the organism is then in a position to transmit this new genetic information to offspring and subsequently to future generations.

The internal factors of evolution must be reassigned their rightful importance if transformative evolution is to be reinstated as a credible theory. It is apparent that empirical research is beginning to rapidly achieve this end and that the findings reviewed in this chapter loosely comprise what might be referred to as a Lamarckian physiological "mechanism" underlying evolution. With continued research, further refinements of our understanding of this mechanism will undoubtedly come about.

We now exit the maze of the microorganismic world and take an overview of some externals of evolution, which offer vistas likely to be more appreciated by the nonspecialist. This realm is as invisible to the unassisted eye as is the microworld, but it is being revealed just as empirically. If biogenetics are the "push" of transformation, perhaps these externals are the "pull."

Chapter Eleven

LIFE FORCE

New ideas have a hard time in science. They tend to be
suppressed by arrogance—condemnation by acknowledged leaders in the field....Dogmatism restrains,
iconoclasm liberates. Vanity, powermongering, ava-
riciousness, pride, dedication, love, industry, sadism
and most other attributes of people apply to science
and to scientists as well.

Carl Lindegren and
Lynn Margulis

From 1935 to 1960, Professor Harold Saxton Burr of Yale University and his associates conducted several hundred studies in which they established the existence of electrical fields that surrounded and permeated all living things, electric fields that organized and controlled the physical, organic matter with which they were associated. Burr's most interesting discovery was that an electric field is set up in the organism at a very early stage, a pure voltage field that seems to originate in the body but to extend a distance from it, and that remains relatively stable, though subject to measurable, temporary changes during pathological processes.[1]

In these findings are the empirical echoes of Bergson's *élan vital*, which, if we remember, is the ubiquitous life force enervating all life forms in the universe. What was once disregarded by mechanistically biased scientists as metaphysical fancy now begins to yield substance in the laboratory.

Burr, in describing his life fields ("L-fields"), uses the analogy of "jelly molds" that shape the myriad millions of living forms on earth. He maintains that L-fields *precede* growth and development, and he substantiates his idea with some arresting experiments. In one of the more interesting, he introduced microelectrodes into a newly laid frog egg and discovered that, *before* the egg was fertilized and began to divide and develop into a tadpole, voltage differences could be detected with marked-out areas that were later to become the nervous system. As Burr rightfully deduced, this pointed to the L-field as an organizer of function and form, a template of sorts.

A thorough investigator, Burr even took measurements from four separate breeds of corn seeds, differing only by a single gene. He called their voltage variance "remarkable and significant," even "profound" as derivations from a parent stock. He concluded logically that this electrical network must correspond strongly to the genetic structure in organisms. Possibly, the electric field was the vehicle for carrying design from the chromosome to the protoplasm.

The electrical basis for practically all organismic activity is already well acknowledged. "Homo electricus" is as good a sobriquet for humans as any, since electrodynamic processes operate in all of our vital systems. The nervous system especially depends upon bioelectrical functions to send sensory information to the brain, and the brain itself must use electrical energy to make sense of this information. Not for nothing has the entire CNS been likened to an electronic computer.

However, the subtler mysteries of electrodynamics in ultimate life functions have barely emerged. Although it is generally agreed that the two are coterminous, some writers claim that physiological functions are preceded by bioelectric or L-fields, as supported by Burr's research. Birth, death, and all vitalities between, they hold, take place in preexistent L-fields. Tissue growth and repair is the most dramatically evident example of duplication in the extant organism and, hence, the best argument for the template or "jelly mold."

But how does the L-field tie in with heredity and evolution? To date there is nothing like a comprehensive answer. It is another of these *how* questions in science and propagates itself with a hundred possible answers. So, in the vagaries of such things as L-fields the best method of quarrying answers seems to be to stick very close to the lab and dig first for facts before designing theories. The conclusions L-field research has established without doubt so far were presented by Dr. Leonard Ravitz at the Fifth International Congress for Hypnosis and Psychosomatic Medicine, held in 1972 in Germany. The electric field, as he defined it, was an *electronic matrix to keep the corporeal form in shape.* Tissue growth and repair in all organisms, as well as birth and death themselves, are regulated by L-fields, according to Ravitz. He stressed the difference between these template fields and other, organ-associated electricity such as the alternating-current output of the brain and heart and epiphenomenal skin resistance.

Thanks to the L-field, said Ravitz, you can recognize your friend's face after many years of absence, in spite of its old molecules having been entirely replaced by new ones. Likewise, many of your own memories remain intact over decades—often for life—even though your brain has been molecularly "replaced" as many as fifty times.[2]

The highlight of Dr. Ravitz's report, not surprisingly, was the conclusion that cellular design is laid out by the L-field rather than the DNA molecule, as previously thought. Tissue is recreated every few years by virtue of the electrodynamic template that molds and holds to form its building blocks.

The actual mechanism(s) by which the cell receives its form from the L-field is, of course, the large *how* of our preceding question on heredity. Answers come by multiples in the microelectric world, and getting at them is as tedious as picking many needles out of the proverbial haystack. In this haystack they are often connected to long ravels of experimental threads. It is exacting work at best.

One important thread seems to be the *ion,* the charged particle that passes electric current through air and solutions. Its function in fertilization and later embryonic development came to light in the periphery of Burr's research. Lord Rothschild and Michael M. Swann in England have suggested that a two-phase voltage block prevents the extra sperm from breaching the egg after the first successful sperm has done so. The first voltage block occurs within several seconds after union but is incomplete; the second is slow and complete.

At the University of California at Los Angeles, Laurinda Jaffe got curious about the fleeting nature of the first voltage block and inserted microelectrodes into a sea-urchin egg. What she found, clarifying

Swann and Rothschild, was that sodium ions flow into the egg immediately after conception, shutting out the polyspermic crowd; the voltage shift in the cell appears akin to a nerve impulse, or some rudiment
of it. Jaffe also discovered that she could inhibit fertilization altogether
by applying extra voltage over the membrane of the virgin egg.[3]

So, another important twofold *how* question was raised: *How*—
and *how far into* the organism's life—does the ionic "thread" regulate
cellular activity? It is common knowledge that potassium, calcium, and
sodium ion levels rise and fall rather predictably in nerve and muscle
activity. Cell division and differentiation also seem to be functions
dependent upon ion levels. For example, in experiments with amphibian embryos, manipulation of sodium ion content has changed skin
cells to nerve cells.

Whether L-fields themselves and other bioelectromagnetic phenomena actually do precurse corporeal, physiological processes in an
ultimately quantifiable way has not yet been determined. Such
authorities as Burr and Ravitz firmly believe they do. Their research
indicates strong evidence for possible sources of a Lamarckian mechanism of transformative evolution. To do so irrefutably, however, further
findings must establish that (1) the genome is potentially sensitive to
"external" (to the genome) organic electrodynamic forces and, provided it is, that (2) the CNS and autonomic nervous system (ANS)
produce electrodynamic fields that influence the genome's processes.

Biophysicist Fritz A. Popp at the University of Hamburg has produced clues in his probes of cellular energy transfer that affirm at least
the first proposition. Nucleic acids, Popp found, are electrical conductors in the cell. They are rendered such by energy excitation above the
critical 3eV (electron volt) level. Because the DNA and RNA macromolecules interact dynamically with their environment, it is
ridiculous, believes Popp, to think of either as in a stationary state. On
the contrary, the DNA helix may act as a resonant circuit, with the DNA
as a coil and the membranes as capacitors connected in parallel, such
as in a tank circuit. Popp sees electromagnetic waves in this context as
quantum information carriers. Photons may carry the ciphers for all
coded functions, including pathologies. Through their exchange (or
that of any other energy quanta), the specific quantitative bursts of
energy needed for DNA coding in the form are delivered.[4]

As to the second proposition, some interesting input comes from
the field of psychosomatics. Theodore Roszak, in his excellent book
Unfinished Animal, notes that thought and emotion have been shown
to produce distinct, and sometimes permanent, alterations in the
body's organ systems. He cites as examples such common psychosomatic disorders as ulcers and acne. Elaborating on this effect, Edward
W. Russell postulates that there exist "thought-fields" ("T-fields")

associated with the brain or mind that interact with L-fields, thereby affecting the electrodynamics of the gene environment. Russell's *Report on Radionics*[5] draws on the work of Dr. Ravitz, who discovered that variations in L-fields correspond consistently to changes in mental states, or consciousness.

Though largely speculative, Russell's extrapolations are lent credence by contemporary biofeedback studies. Other studies now reveal that the brain generates low-level biomagnetic fields (detectable by cryogenic sensors, in the form of "magnetoencephalograms"). There is also measurable evidence that the mind can "think" the body into and out of illness. Repeated correlations have been found, for instance, between psychological factors and the occurrence of cancer. Doctors such as Carl Simonton in Texas are using imagery (T-fields?) and other mental techniques in helping their patients retard the growth of this and other diseases. They report dramatic reversals in a number of cases, unexplainable by other factors.

One leading theory in modern cancer research holds that the malignancy may be prompted by a malfunction in the body's immunological defenses. And immunological reactions may involve a learning or experiential factor in which antibodies are "educated" to recognize specific antigens, with the resulting experience stored in memory. Cancer itself appears to be caused by some dysynchronization in the cells' DNA/RNA organization, maintenance, and growth.

Although adaptative specialization is the handmaiden of evolution, she can be a lethal servant under stress. The intricate immune system is perhaps the area where advantage and hazard are at once most incipient in the extreme. The specialized servants of adaptation must function in a balanced environment (perhaps synonymous with the L-field) if they are to serve and not undermine the "master."

Wherever the "governor-general" of evolution ultimately resides, it is accurate to say that its directorship is nothing like a strict top-down affair. The genetic mandate must be subject to checks and balances on all sides, or above and below, if you prefer. Most probably it is contained by the very field that it takes a catalytic part in creating. If an organism's overall organization can be likened to a sociopolitical unit, then it indeed resembles a republic more than an autocracy. This is close to D. G. Garan's view, who describes it in the standard terms of physics. He invites us to picture "super-imposed layers around the genetic center." Pressure or resistance encountered by any one layer will force that layer below it to "evolve additional compensatory pathways"—that is to say, new outlets for the increased pressure. Evolutionary adaptation thus proceeds top to bottom, bottom to top, the genetic center shaping the organism while being shaped itself by changes in the larger organism.[6]

Garan speaks of the "genetic self" or center, but hints that centers exist on levels above or below the gene. Thus functions are accompanied by a required form, and here we are back to our prior considerations of design. *Morphogenetics* (the "coming-into-being" of forms) is a current hotbed of controversy.

The ideas of Dr. Rupert Sheldrake, a plant physiologist, are helping to revolutionize our understanding of morphogenesis. His views, based on reliable, if unfinalized, discoveries, have thoroughly provoked the scientific establishment in the best tradition of creative thought. That the opposition has come out so strongly against him is proof enough that his views are well worth training an open mind upon.

In his recent book *A New Science of Life*,[7] Sheldrake goes back to ask a basic question: How does an organism acquire its shape over time? His incendiary answer is quite unorthodox, and by the cracks and pops of the hot argument, some dry wood must be going up in smoke. On the surface, Dr. Sheldrake's answer to the morphogenetic riddle seems so far outside mainstream theories that it is called radical by critics and supporters alike—and certainly it is in terms of this century's scientific *Zeitgeist*. Sheldrake elegantly christens the concept "the hypothesis of formative causation."

To understand this hypothesis we are required to range yet further into the physics of evolution. This time we must venture into the eminently possible realms he refers to as "morphogenetic fields." An approach to these fields can be made mentally by roughly picturing them as broad-spectrumed, interlinked electrodynamic systems, of which L-fields are perhaps locally specialized subsystems. A crudely useful metaphor is the radio or television network. Electrical impulses are transmitted and received by apparati capable of composing and recomposing them into messages and images. In the bioelectric context analogous messages and images could be sent out and received by individuals or whole species that are on the same "wave-length."

The concept of course is not new, as Sheldrake admits. It has been around as long as the electronic media. But his application of it to morphogenetics is imaginative and creative. He proposes that the fields are not merely communications systems but complex, pervasive patterns of electromagnetic current that actually transfer and/or impose design on all organic and inorganic matter. In other words they are the bestowers of generalized form, the supra-templates for some functional level of the "archetype."

Why this conception appears radical, even to Sheldrake himself, is that it proffers solutions for troublesome genetic puzzles unanswerable by conventional Lamarckian and Darwinian outlooks alike. For both rest essentially on linear-hereditary models of evolution. They view formal change as fundamentally sequenced along a one-dimensional time-line. Their logic is based on what could be called the "clock model." The gene is the clock, and mutational events necessarily occur separately and successively on the face of it. In heredity the collective effects of these events are passed down from unit to unit, parent to offspring.

Evolutionists of both persuasions share the picture of the gene as the workshop wherein the sole molds of physical change are found. The great difference between Darwinism and Lamarckism, however, is in their diametrically opposing ideas of causality. Whereas the former attributes mutation to random fortuity, the latter interprets it as the consequence of purpose and continuity.

Obviously, rigid adherence to either of these linear-based models will dismiss as inconcrete—or perhaps fanciful—any extralinear evidence that suggests contradictions to the models, such as that uncovered by Sheldrake's research and theory.

If Sheldrake's hypothesis is correct, it means that the genes and their constituents are something like integrated circuits within the transmitting and receiving organisms. It may also mean that telepathy and other paranormal phenomena are not anomalous but pervasive. Lastly, it could form the basis for a "lateral" model of evolution, which at bottom may nonetheless be complementary to a linear one. Sheldrake himself seems to see them as contradictory, perhaps because he has not fully perceived the possible links between them.

The implications for learning and behavior are immense. If "morphic resonance" is indeed everything Dr. Sheldrake believes it to be, many puzzles associated with these processes can eventually be resolved—perhaps sooner than expected.

Returning to the empirical realm, let us review several cases of the kind that have stumped the genetic detectives.

In a paper titled "Some Unusual Aspects of Communication," Edward Campbell relates an unusual experience that once transpired between himself and two lionesses he had trained (without the use of punishment) to perform circus acts. After becoming "good friends" with the cats, he was later called in to military service. After six months' absence, he returned on leave to pay them a visit. With the circus under way and the two animals in holding cages, they were immediately able to sense Campbell's presence even though they couldn't see him or smell him. They oriented in his exact direction in an "attitude of extreme alertness" while he stood outside the circus building peering at them through a minute spyhole far away and with 200 to 250 people between them. As soon as he entered the circus building, with the crowd still between them and he wearing an RAF uniform which they had never seen before, the lionesses—who still could not see him—"suddenly went into a frenzy." Campbell, as well as witnesses, were quite certain that some form of telepathic event had occurred.

Most of us are familiar with the "breakthrough" principle, wherein a novel achievement, considered virtually impossible by observers before its performance, becomes commonplace *en masse* as time passes. (An example is the simultaneous, yet independent rediscovery of Mendel's laws of heredity by three different groups of scientists in three different countries in 1900.) But how does the creative contagion spread where there is no visibly physical connection? What is the medium of communication between man and two African lionesses? Or rats in different mazes? Sheldrake asserts that the causative-formation hypothesis offers plausible descriptions of these phenomena in a biological framework. What's more, he believes it can be tested by standard experiment. The most promising would be tests of animal learning, for example teaching randomly selected rats a task that has never been performed by rats before. Subsequent groups of rats worldwide, says Sheldrake, "should be able to learn the same task more easily, even in the absence of any physical connection or communication."[9]

The assumption is *ex post facto*, as its author well knows. But its validity warrants it. Rat-maze studies have been conducted that offer such evidence. The most extensive were conducted by American psychologist William McDougall at Harvard University in the early 1900s. Hoping to gather clinical support for the Lamarckian principle of inheritance of acquired characteristics, McDougall's experiments extended through 49 rat generations, lasting 16 years. He reported that the "later generations showed an increased facility, measured by a reduction in the amount of training required by nearly 90 percent."[10]

McDougall was sure that this demonstrated inheritance of an acquired characteristic and reaffirmed that evolution was purposive, not the result of random, mechanical processes. He also believed that his studies "lent strong support to the idea of a non-material basis for racial as well as individual memory."[11]

Anticipating his Darwinian critics who might accuse him of initially selecting quicker-learning rats for use in his study, McDougall stressed that all of his animals were chosen at random. He even went to the trouble of running control studies in which he specifically began with a group of the slowest-learning rats. In this case the logic of genetic selection might produce a decrease in the rate of learning.

However, even the slow-witted rat lines seemed bent on improving their stock over time. Generational improvements were noted. Much later on, other researchers—A. E. Crew of Edinburgh and W. E. Agar and associates in Melbourne—repeated McDougall's experiments, using the same type of water maze. Both surprisingly found that the first generations of rats learned much faster than even McDougall's later generations had done. Indeed, a number of Crew's rats ran the maze perfectly on the first try.

The telling difference between McDougall's and Crew and Agar's studies stemmed from a single point of procedure. The latter also ran control lines that also improved over time, but these were descended from rats that had never run the maze—thus, a doubtful correlation between genetic factors (of the acquired kind) and maze skills. It would therefore seem that McDougall's findings were validated by Crew and Agar, though theirs opened questions on his deductions. Certainly they seemed to vindicate Sheldrake's view.

Whether these later studies run counter to Lamarckian theory must at present remain a matter of interpretation. It could well be that rats in the untrained control line were merely improving in time due to an experimental artifact, as yet undiscovered. Perhaps they were better fed over the long run of generations. It is common knowledge that increases in size and strength are general to many species, including our own. We also know that human swimming speeds are increasing, and so it may be with rats in water mazes.

Ultimately all acquired characteristics must register in the genetic code of the organism. In terms of evolution this is what differentiates one species from another, or from its ancestral species. It is eminently reasonable to conclude that evolution might proceed by a vector combination of Lamarckian and Sheldrakian factors. Darwin is the "odd man out" in such a scheme, for random processes make a poor showing in rat-mazes, or any other environments that demand memory, learning, and purpose.

The evidence for bioelectric field properties emanating from the "genetic self" (Garan's term) is dramatically displayed during embryologic and morphogenic development. Dr. Lewis Wolpert has addressed himself to the problem of how embryonic cells differentiate and organize in space. It is standard procedure, he relates, for the principles of organization and orientation to be understood as operating in the conceptual dynamics of a "field." This includes reference to gradients, polarity, forces, balances, boundary regions, and so forth.

Wolpert notes that the use of a general field concept is clinically practical—it accounts for the observed phenomena. Its "positional information" lends more substance to such earlier ideas as embryonic fields, defining the specific coordinating systems of regulation and development.[12] Less technically, the morphogenetic field is no more fantastic than, say, a gravitational field. Perhaps it is the abundant amount of timid thinking on the subject that is fantastical, what psychologist Ashley Montague refers to as "psychosclerosis."

Wolpert himself avoids calling morphogenetic fields "electrodynamic" in nature, although his writings draw that obvious conclusion. He does intimate that a new level of analysis is sorely needed and that orthodox biological viewpoints are inadequate. He admits residual frustration with reductionistic approaches (whereby cellular behavior is defined as the effects of molecular mechanisms), and he also acknowledges a need for a new phenomenology that will enable himself and other biogeneticists to define "what we are trying to explain and where to look for the explanation." Wolpert's most definitive—and radical—revision, however, is offered as this statement: "Perhaps we should be less apologetic and remember that the study of genetics was (and is) effective at levels other than the level of DNA."[13]

Less apologetic? Modern scientists are not overly disposed to audacity. Too many of them seem to equate skepticism along with conservatism or diffidence, and probably that is why Sheldrake comes across as a rampant renegade. If he were not an international authority, of course, his ideas would be quickly shunted out of the field. But he is, and they will not be. It is an intellectual unpleasantry to think how many bold and creative ideas have been so easily dismissed. Hopefully, the trend is being reversed.

Dr. Bernard Dixon is another authority who thinks that field theory such as Sheldrake's may have much to contribute to our understanding of morphogenetics, at least at the biochemical level. He too trains on the cell's marvelous structural development from fertilization (the product of sperm-ovum fusion) to final organismic maturation. The computer program simile for the DNA blueprint is, Dixon maintains, a poor model for describing "what actually happens, let alone the details." How do genetically identical cells ("clones" from the fertilized original) differentiate into tissue, blood, muscle, toenail, or dental pulp? he asks. In agreement with Sheldrake, he will not be satisfied with "vague suggestions about physiochemical interactions in time and space."[14]

Like those found in biochemistry and morphogenetics, the deep enigmas of nature have historically outlived theories that have been left only vaguely developed. Imagine William Harvey mincing words when he set forth his hypothesis of the circulatory system. Or picture Albert Einstein afraid of making waves with his revolutionary theory of relativity. In short, humility is not timidity. All outstanding innovators have been devoid of the latter, and they have often exercised the former in their inner self-honesty, regardless of the criticism of those who in reality lacked it.

Curiously enough, more than a few authorities in the biological sciences since McDougall have held views similar to his and

Sheldrake's but have not carried them to the firing line of controversy. Several have ventured into print, however.

Sir Alister Hardy—late president of the British Association for the Advancement of Science and influential member of the Society for Psychical Research—was one of the few eminent zoologists of his time who took serious notice of McDougall's rat-maze experiments. In *The Living Stream* he suggested that internal factors may be quite as important as environmental ones in evolution. Like Sheldrake, he was interested in telepathic communication, speculating that if "impressions of design, form and experience" can on occasion be mentally relayed between human individuals, then a "general subconscious sharing of form and behavior pattern—some sort of a psychic blueprinting" could conceivably take place via telepathic dynamics. General and rapid habit changes spread throughout an entire species, improbably accounted for by mere physical contact, would be obvious evidence for such telepathy.

Hardy presents his ideas on telepathy in somewhat hesitant language, typical of scientists who do not want to be accused of toe-dipping at the edge of the occult.[15] It is almost as if he is asking permission to voice his thought. He need not, however, considering that certain laws of physics, as they are applicable to living organisms, have little to do with the occult, especially when such considerations adhere to empirical principles. On the other hand, automatic aversion to the unfamiliar, be it scientific or otherwise, may be closer to primitivism than some instances of "metaphysical inflation," to borrow a term from psychologist Robert Ornstein.

Hardy's speculations in this direction have encouraged a new breed of biological scientists who are daring to explore any field relevant to their disciplines, including the morphogenetic. For example, Lyall Watson, a gifted biologist, takes up among other subjects the case of telepathic influence in his fascinating book *Lifetide*. His elegant ruminations paved the way in part for Sheldrake's expansions:

> ... We are governed partly by nuclear DNA and partly by something else....In the present state of our knowledge about this something else, it would be rash to assume it is based on a unitary factor like a gene. It does in some ways seem like a complex set of influences which function in a variety of different ways....I see it as something which has a collective, rather than a personal nature, being part of a wider perspective, without the selfish interest of the genes....
>
> I believe the contingent system operates in the areas of decision where only a slight shift in equilibrium is sufficient to produce

dramatic changes of direction. Like gravity, it is almost too weak to
be measured and yet too powerful to be ignored. Contingents may
affect genetic and embryological processes and be influential in this
way in determining phenotype, but I suggest that their major influence over our lives lies in cooperation and competition with the
nuclear gene system, and that it is this interaction which results in
the development of mind.[16]

With the substitution of just a few words, Watson could be speaking of
a shift in scientific philosophy itself. The "development of mind" he
alludes to ultimately requires a wider perspective that would indeed
"produce dramatic changes of direction." Be it gene mutation, mental
telepathy, or scientific progress, all evolutionary processes are by definition ones of enlargement and elaboration.

Aside from its hypothetical practicality, the concept of the morphogenetic field may help serve the Western culture's urgent need to
recover its lost identity in nature. Westerners are beginning to realize
that their random exploitation of nature inexorably debases and threat-
ens their own collective existence. This is brought on by their general
ignorance of what Native Americans refer to as "the great web of life."

Rich images such as the Web of Life invite us to see nature in
wholes instead of parts, and to perceive the actual or potential links
between all organic and inorganic beings. The major Eastern esoteric
traditions all have at their center some variation of the Web-of-Life
principle. Bergson's *élan vital* might be the electrodynamic life force
that flows through the web, sustaining and propagating its unitary
forms and perhaps, as Dr. Sheldrake insists, shaping them.

One error of modern science has been its premature thirst to apply
immutable physical laws to nature from a time-bound, terrestrial perspective. Certain of these, such as gravity, were until the 20th century
thought to be unchangeable and beyond time. Somehow this outlook
led to a static picture of physical phenomena, subject to permutation
and change but generally mechanical and resistant to it. But then, anything static is simpler to study.

Einstein's Theory of Relativity was a big step toward changing all
that. Now the hypothesis of causative formation has extended its logic
to morphogenetics. The causative electrodynamic fields may operate in
and span time, themselves being manifested and extended by earth-
bound factors, the first being local outputs of consciousness, perhaps
the "T-fields."

The Web of Life is an open-ended ecological tapestry still being
created. Its basic structure is already laid out, but its future designs
cannot be said to be predetermined. If its archetypal plan resides in
some immutable, eternal sphere, that plan is being particularized in

uniqueness by earth essences and factors. Morphogenetic fields might feasibly represent preexistent potentials that are actualized by evolutionary drives. Every mutation or transmutation is a break in the extant symmetry in order to create a new one. Thus nature is dynamic, inviting design upon design, infinitely. All interstices between the lines of symmetry must by this reasoning be fields of potentiality, morphogenetic possibility. Asymmetry would then be the break-point.

In Spain there is a 14th-century Moorish fortress called the Alhambra, the interior of which is embellished with intricate, marvelous mosaics. A crystallographer touring it in the 1800s was given an astonishing aesthetic surprise: he had seen the *same* patterns under his microscope. The conclusion was obvious: crystal patterns can at least be "thought of" before they are actualized. Since crystal patterns seem to be among the most fortuitous, unpredictable designs in nature, this was a paradox indeed. But it is known that once a chemical is synthesized, it seems to become easier to synthesize it again in subsequent attempts. The new crystal design appears to perpetrate its own existence (in this instance with the aid of human consciousness). This is where Sheldrake's logic has taken him, at any rate. And no one has yet been able to counter it.

We are vastly indebted to all of these pioneers in the morphogenetic field for revivifying the concept of *élan vital* and breathing new life into evolutionary theory. But to Professor Burr must go the special credit for detecting its very physics, long years spent by him in the lab quantifying its elusive but quite corporeal electric voltage. With the recent use of electrostimulation as a medical tool (in diminishing pain and speeding the healing of bones), Burr's once-heretical findings and ideas are now more easily appreciated within establishment circles. Nonetheless, the implications of bioelectrical processes within the context of organic evolution are yet to be fully apprehended.

Chapter Twelve

THE EVOLVING BRAIN

*The exponential growth of the human brain during the
last two hundred and fifty thousand years is unique in
the history of evolution. Even today we lack a satisfac-
tory explanation how it came about.*

Richard Restak,
The Brain: The Last Frontier

When it comes to describing the powers of the human brain, even the most conservative of scientific writers are forced to wax superlative. "The last great frontier," "an evolutionary wonder," "an awesome memory bank" are all commonplace expressions. They are apt descriptions, for the simple fact is that the organ of reason in Homo sapiens is the most highly organized 3½ pounds of matter on earth. How it got that way, however, is anything but simple. Even the currently popular model of the brain as a "supercomputer" is only a mild approximation.

Dr. Robert Ornstein, the distinguished brain physiologist, has described the wholly unique impression that was his when, as a lab student, he first took a human brain in hand. And for him the novelty of that singular experience has never worn off. That entity in each of our heads is indeed a marvelous thing, which we all want to know more about. There are dozens of good publications (books, journals, articles, etc.) on brain physiology, structure, and function now available to the general reader; however, only some of the research (much of it now popular knowledge) that is pertinent to the study of evolution can be included here.

Humans have the highest brain-to-body ratio of any animal. That is, our species is the most "brainy" in terms of density alone. More interesting—and undoubtedly less well known—recent research clearly shows that creative, choice-demanding activities virtually increase brain volume. Thus the matchless brain-to-body ratio of humans is handily accounted for: the higher reaches of evolution call for more brains and less brawn, and at an increasing rate. However, even among rats, monkeys, and other animals, the same phenomenon of brain challenge stimulating an increase in brain complexity has been recorded. Brains of individuals inhabiting stimulating environments tend to be measurably superior in size and intelligence to those that are stimulus-starved, even though their diets be equal. But what mechanism(s) account for this?

A human brain is constructed of roughly 10 billion neurons, or nerve cells. Each one of these 10 billion has a potential of making 10^{28} interconnections in the surrounding network—thousands of times per second. Providing one had eons of time and galaxies full of ink and paper, this number could be represented by a 1 trailed by nearly 10 million miles of zeroes. And since choice making and problem solving put extra demands on the brain, this kind of mentation requires vast numbers of new neural connections (via axon conductors to axon terminals to receptor dendrites), which in turn requires the creation of additional neural material, and thus extra density. Brain volume then tends to gradually increase (over many eons) in order to accommodate the new mass. The brain gets heavier and larger.

Why the most human part of the brain, the cerebral cortex, has continued its ballooning development far beyond basic survival needs is a question that has not been adequately addressed by Darwinists. Implicit in their *crambe repetita* reasoning is that nature is excessive, and often ultraexcessive ("nature abhors a vacuum"); it must have lots of material for experiment. But why should nature continue such ultra-excess in the human brain when humankind's survival was so long ago ensured? Since the Darwinists themselves maintain that survival modes are determined by random and beneficial mutations of structure, what can be the purpose of all that extra brain? Does it not constitute an excessive kind of waste that nature must abhor as much as a vacuum? But the question produces the standard Darwinian answer, and the answer leads us right back to the same question. Like the survival-of-the-fittest doctrine, the tautology is apparent. After all is said and resaid the Darwinists, with all their sophisticated jargon, cannot explain the human brain. (Even Darwin himself admitted this to his co-developer of the natural-selection theory, Alfred Wallace.) Actually, that which is totally absent in Darwinian doctrine—consciousness and mind—likely has a great deal to do with "overdevelopments" like the human brain; however, these intangibles cannot easily be fitted into an ultrascientific, reductionistic-materialistic framework and, hence, they are rejected outright even as conceivable hypotheses.

But let us look again at the anatomy of the human brain. It is certainly economical in the extreme in terms of space. Inside the cranium most of the brain's bulk nestles snugly in multiple folds, creating an ovular network of well-defined fissures. Yet unfolded, the surface would exceed *two square feet*. We can begin to understand the fascination and wonder felt by Dr. Ornstein and so many others. The brain is a world of its own whose mystery has just begun to be plumbed—a mystery accented by the deep longitudinal fissure that divides the brain into its distinct left and right hemispheres. The two halves are joined at the bottom of this fissure by a bundle of 200 million nerve fibers called the *corpus callosum*. The functional specialization of these hemispheres will be discussed shortly, but first a sketch of the brain's vertical evolution.

Technically, the brain is one of two components of the central nervous system. The other is the spinal column that classifies all vertebrates. The *brain stem* crowns the spinal column and is the first nodular manifestation of the brain. This is the primitive brain of reptiles, which represents the first true adaptation of dry-land evolution beyond the amphibians. It serves mostly as a basic arouser, to keep the organism at least as active as any three-toed sloth. The next development is the *limbic system* or "mammalian brain." At this stage we find the classic "animalistic" drives, reflexes, and instincts characterized by reactionary emotion and behavior. Motivation is totally preprogrammed; "fight or flight" is the apt catch-phrase describing this program. When the organism is not satisfying its basic needs (sex, sleep, food, drink, self-defense, etc.), excesses tend to show up in social interaction. The higher mammals, especially primates, display these propensities in greed, gluttony, overaggressiveness, selfishness, jealousy, and sometimes paranoia. "Living in the limbic system" in one sense means living with various addictions, activities involving pleasure seeking and pain avoidance.

We now reach the peak of the brain world with the *cerebral cortex* or cerebrum, which nearly completes the system in the higher primates (monkeys, apes, and humans). The cerebrum is supported by the *cerebellum*, a kind of minibrain attached to the base of the major organ. The cerebellum has evolved parallel with the cerebrum and, until fairly recently, was thought to serve merely as a backup system for motor function (i.e., coordination). However, new research has found an increasing role for it as a comonitor of emotion and sensation to the limbic system. The cerebellum is just over 10 percent of the weight of the cerebrum, but unfurled it reveals two thirds of the cerebrum's volume. Some scientists now suggest that the cerebellum is mainly a satellite of psychic subconsciousness, feeding back to the cerebrum the contents of dreams, trance states, extrasensory information, and so on. Whatever its significance, it is newly explored territory.

It is the cerebral cortex, however, that contains the paradoxical complexities of consciousness. This "gray matter" has been a puzzle to speculation for a long time, yet brilliant research and theory in the past decade has greatly clarified the puzzle, and a coherent picture is beginning to emerge.

A milestone in brain physiology was made over a century ago when it was found that lesions of the left side of the cortex impair language processing in right-handed people, while lesions of the right side do not. The pioneering work by such specialists as Roger Sperry and Robert Ornstein confirmed this effect and also established that the right side controls spatial and perceptual abilities. Brain study cast off the last vestigial fallacies of phrenology, and consciousness became a 20th-century science.

Fundamentally, the right-brain is in charge of nonsequential or holistic cognition. This all-at-once mode of function is associated with insight, intuition, and initial recognition of shapes and forms. Art, invention, and all instances of original creativity are the glories of this realm. The left hemisphere "idles" during these episodes of inspiration, but kicks into gear again when they are gone. Computation, logical-linear thought, or verbal analysis might then be called upon for the verification or description of the original idea. Often they complete it. The two modes are therefore complimentary. All of us use both alternately many times a day in mundane activities. Recognizing a face or telephone number is, for example, a right-hemisphere function, while writing down the name of the face or dialing the number sets the left side ticking. These effects have been graphically proven in numerous EEG (electroencephalogram) experiments performed by Professor Ornstein and others. When given linear tasks such as letter writing, subjects produced a high increase of alpha rhythms in the left lobe, indicating switched-on activity there. Beta waves in the right lobe showed it to be at relative rest. Conversely, when the subject was given a spatial task such as reconstructing abstract block designs, the rhythms were reversed.

The shortcomings of Western education have been highlighted by modern brain research. Study after study in the fields of psychology and learning underscores the verdict: the left side of the brain is overtrained in the classroom while right-hemisphere specialties—inventiveness, creativity, intuition, perception—suffer delimiting atrophy. Verbal, technical, and logical skills are considered more crucial for the average student than are those "diversions" of art, dance, music, theatre, and so forth. But the failure to develop the right brain with the left results in both psychic and intellectual imbalance. Behavioral and learning disorders in abundance are the product. The high premium placed on technology and rationality is now seen to be taking an equally high toll in human fulfillment.

The recent interest by psychologists and educators in methods to develop the right hemisphere in those who are not nominally artistic or inventive is certainly a positive trend in this state of affairs. As more and more people learn to make use of their right brains, greater freedom from mechanicalness and the narrower perspectives of the muscle-bound left hemisphere will occur. Much tunnel vision will be replaced by "world vision."

The brain is not widely thought of as a pattern-making system. Dr. Edward de Bono of Cambridge University was one of the first scientists to completely define this primary process and to point out that the human "thinking cap" is vastly underused as such. As a successful inventor and writer, he is quite qualified to make that claim. De Bono's basic premise is that, as a pattern-making system, the brain or mind continually attempts to fit new or unusual information into the familiar matrix of prior experience. The process is automatic and subtle, and occurs quickly—at the instant of perception when the unexpected situation is encountered. This predisposition to frame the unfamiliar into the familiar pattern or matrix is known as "mental set." Mental sets dominate our thought and behavior in the routines of life. The major drawback of the mental set is that it is a form of mechanicalness (habit) that frequently prevents us from choosing the most useful option in a situation. But if mental sets are minimized, mental patterns will then be altered as needed, opening up broad new vistas for personal and collective evolution.

It has been estimated by brain experts that most of us use only 10 to 20 percent of our total brain capacity. Undoubtedly, our minds are needlessly confined by inflexible habits, patterns, and mechanicalness. Traditional schooling in the West has conclusively reinforced these rigid sets and in some areas even literally created them. Attitudes themselves are mental sets that reflect psychic dynamics at the deepest level. And today's teachers and parents bemoan the widespread "bad attitude" of youth both inside and outside the classroom. Is this bad attitude conceivably an honest response to something gone woefully amiss? Psychology has been answering yes to that question.

The bilateral nature of the brain subserves the multidimensionality inherent in the nature of mind itself (de Bono's "lateral thinking" techniques being a practical application of that fact). It should be reemphasized that, although the brain seems to polarize cognition into two distinct modes, its actual use of the two is the antithesis of reductionism. This was long ago intimated by the fact that some severely brain-damaged people could be rehabilitated to lead normal lives. Research on animals and humans demonstrated that some areas of the brain could take over and compensate for regions that were heavily damaged or removed altogether. Quite surprisingly, many animal subjects and human patients who have had sections of their brains surgically removed go on to lead almost totally functional lives. This amazing compensatory potential alone makes the brain a most marvelous and unique organ, and—as we shall now see—a unique theory has recently been proposed to explain it.

In 1947, Dennis Gabor invented the three-dimensional photographic technique of holography. This breakthrough enables us to comprehend how the brain functions. It is indeed a stupendous memory and image bank, but it is qualitatively different from a mechanical "supercomputer" or any other closed system of digit-based artificial intelligence. Though it is true that today's computers are wonders of digitized and stored technical data (and computers now even play passingly fair chess), they are still helpless idiot savants in the multidimensional realms of creativity and holistic, practical problem solving. The computer does not actually open up new information; instead it simply serves up, quickly, bits and combinations of its preprogrammed contents. Valuable as that service is, computers in themselves do not really "figure" a solution to a problem, much less make meaning outside a narrow context. Only the mind-brain does that—through the principle of the hologram, as many theorists are saying.

The holonomic brain model is the creation of the brilliant surgeon and neuropsychologist Karl Pribram of Stanford University. In brief, the holographic effect itself is produced in this way: a laser beam is split, one half of it directed to the holographic film (the "reference beam"), the other deflected off the object to be photographed. When the two wavefronts intersect on the film, an "interference pattern" is recorded as a miniature frozen puddle of light-and-dark ripples. This is the coded memory of the object-light event. The same principle operates when two rocks are dropped into a pond and their ripples trough and crest. If the water could be frozen, it would be a kind of holographic "film." Finally, when a later laser beam (identical to the reference beam) illuminates the film, the object is reconstructed as a three-dimensional image.

Pribram posits that memories may be stored in our brains in the same way. In addition, he points out that these psychic holograms can be superimposed on one another infinitely, activated into images by the "laser beams" of specific stimulations. Remember also, as we mentioned in an early chapter, the holographic plate is brainlike in that shattered fragments of it can each reconstitute the whole image. Pribram maintains that the brain compensates for injury in like manner. He goes on to suggest that the elusive entity called mind residing in each of our brains is a unique, individualized coding of a collective mind-at-large. "Racial memory," the "collective unconscious," and like concepts may, in the holonomic analogy, represent archetypical images in an almost literal sense.

If, as Pribram says, the brain is the organic equivalent of a hologram, then the ideas of a modular universe and cosmic consciousness are as close to scientific significance as General Relativity or Quantum Theory. Indeed, it reinforces them. For all three turn on the concept of mind. And if the brain is the central locus and transformer of evolutionary energy on earth, the implications of its holonomic importance have barely begun to be realized.

Chapter Thirteen

GLOBAL BRAIN

Genetic mutation is not, it would seem, due to chance,
but directed in some way, perhaps toward a spiritual
regeneration of humanity—a bridge, as it were,
between a lower, and a higher level of consciousness.

Louis Pauwels and
Jacques Bergier,
The Morning of the Magicians

Contemporary studies of human problem-solving skills leave little empirical doubt that the typically functioning human individual calls into play but a minor portion of his potential cerebral ability; informed estimates are put at 20 percent or less. What this cognitive quiescence bodes for the human species' next collective evolutionary step cannot be known precisely at this point. Some speculations can be made, however, that are eminently warranted in the context of transformist theory. What a human "new brain" in this sense might be will also be discussed.

It is a popular but mistaken notion that brain size (i.e., volume and mass) has continually increased in human evolution right up to the present time. In fact, the modern human's brain is no larger than that of Neanderthal, who lived about 75,000 years ago. If we accept that phylogenetic (species) brain size is determined by evolutionary necessity, then we can surmise why the *Homo sapiens* brain is not larger than Neanderthal's: because the *Homo sapiens* species has not made collective maximum use of the organ it has. Anyone who thinks that a bigger brain would automatically make the race more intelligent is not unlike the resident of a mansion who believes he needs to build more rooms, not realizing that behind its many closed doors 80 percent of its space is sitting vacant. What may now be needed is not an enlarged brain structure, but an *expanded* brain function—a "new mind." This is simply a conclusion of the transformist hypothesis that mental dynamics precede and effect morphogenetic ones.

What is the role, the purpose, of such a "new mind" in the broader scheme of terrestrial and universal evolution? To answer, it is necessary to draw certain panoramic analogies of structure and function on these scales. These analogies are not new; incipient in various Eastern philosophies for centuries, they are currently elaborated on by respected Western thinkers in a number of fields.

The idea of a global mind-brain has taken a strong hold in evolutionary theory in the West, developed by such theorists as Teilhard de Chardin (the "noosphere") and James Lovelock ("Gaia Hypothesis").

Recent explications of planetary consciousness (e.g., the "Global Brain" of Peter Russell) define the earth as a developing organism, intricately structured vertically and laterally, with corresponding degrees of intelligence and organization. Humankind, the evolutionary apex of this rich, vibrant, living mosaic, can be viewed as its central nervous system. The culmination of this biospheric CNS is the most evolved and intelligent humans on the planet, the brain cells, so to speak. This earth "brain" is still maturing, the neuron-individuals progressively expanding their function in concert with each other and guiding the earth-body to higher evolutionary levels.

Within the framework of a modular universe, humanity's earth-bred consciousness can be analogized as an energy (which, in a sense, it indeed is) being increasingly refined and expanded and seeking release from its present planetary confines. Where does it go from here? This question is already being answered by the advent of space exploration. The global mind-brain is reaching out into interplanetary space, perhaps one day even interstellar or intergalactic space, possibly to make contact in material or immaterial modes with other forms of intelligence. A universe in evolution would without question require such a panoply of interacting intelligences. In space flight and telecommunications we see the pattern commencing on a local level (our solar system), human "cells" linking up in ever-expanding and interlocking networks, very like the literal neurons of the brain.

Eastern cosmologies regard evolutionary processes as ascending on a gradient from lower, physical levels to higher, nonphysical ones; that is, from material to spiritual evolution. What we experience as "consciousness" is some intermediate stage, like one wavelength of light on a vast spectrum. For humans, it may well be that the physical body and brain have no evolutionary need of significant structural change, perhaps the reason why we are not so anatomically different from Neanderthal and Cro-Magnon. Still, new brain structure may evolve when full use is made of the present *whole* brain. And knowing that we do not use all of our mental capacity, we can regard much of our 50,000-year-old brain as "new" already.

A thematic thread running throughout this book has been the interconnectedness of all things. This is not to say, however, that all possible connections are consummated in full, or detectable to an observer outside of the immediate "system" when they are. Relativistic physics has taught us something of the macro aspect of this complex phenomenon, formulated by Heisenberg's Principle of Uncertainty in this way: an observer cannot be completely, objectively detached from that which he observes, because his very act of observation establishes a contact that in some—often extremely subtle—way alters the dynamics of the observed subject. We mention this principle in passing because it seems fundamentally bound up with that of dimensional perspective, which in turn is aligned with that of hierarchical intelligence. Some of the more esoteric, "occult" aspects in the idea of hidden knowledge can be apprehended in these relationships, including certain traditions associated with belief in unseen powers guiding human destiny. The issues of free will versus predetermined fate can be resolved in a fuller understanding of the nature of the evolutionary ascent of consciousness.

It is assumed that greater or lesser dimensions of perspective, perception, and comprehension determine the various grades of universal intelligence. These are the very factors that constitute knowing in the full sense, independent of logical reasoning. Therefore, consciousness in general on one level will not experience, by definition, the reality of those levels superior to it. In fact, we can venture that an inferior level may be almost totally psychically blind to its immediate superior. Do apes in the wild know about humans? Does a salamander contemplate lizardhood? We can safely say that the consciousness of the lizard is more capable of "knowing about" the salamander than vice versa, since the lizard has long passed through the stage of amphibian. But the amphibian has yet to know the special experience of being a reptile, with a reptile's superior consciousness.

Nonetheless, according to transformist precepts, there is an evolutionary spearhead within each stratum of intelligence that serves as the forerunner in the advancement of the corresponding species or subspecies up to the succeeding level. In the case of humanity this minority contingent would be represented by all of the known and unknown sages, saints, prophets, and authentic "masters" of the ages. In the prementioned scheme, these individuals might be compared to the most evolved brain cells, perhaps collectively forming the seminal beginnings of a new human mind. In the Sufi tradition this group is referred to as the "inner circle" of humanity. Figuratively, the most evolved person or persons therein would constitute the very tip of the spearhead.

Reassuming the continuum of interacting and interdependent degrees of consciousness in the universe, and further supposing that a superior degree is in some sense (let us say "magnetic") the guide of its inferior degree to increased consciousness and intelligence, what might be conjectured about the *modus operandi* of humanity's evolutionary guidance? In the plant and animal kingdom it would appear to be the biological compulsion of survival and reproductive drives, but with humans another, new, factor enters the picture. Hard put for any neat definition, we can do no better than to quote one exceptionally succinct writer:

> The direction imposed on man is only relatively coercive. Because of the high energies which are potential in him, man may not be compulsively directed. Means have to be employed which do not outrage the integrity of his potential nature.
>
> This is achieved by arranging a bias in favor of those situations which contain developmental possibilities and by limiting man's *opportunities* for making involuntary choices.
>
> About this line there may be *marginal interplay of determinism and free will* [our italics].[1]

Chapter Fourteen

CONSCIOUSNESS EVOLVING

The yen to become wanderers among the stars involves more than the need to satisfy a cosmic curiosity. Basically, it flows out of an instinctive need to evolve. We belong to an unfinished species. We have limitless capacities for growth; indeed, our uniqueness lies in our ability to steer our own evolution. The destination becomes visible through an enlarged perspective. The greatest adventure within the reach of a sentient species is seeing itself in an expanding relationship.

Norman Cousins,
Human Options

Consciousness.

To be sure, an unempirical word, a veritable maze of meanings. Yet it is reluctantly resorted to as an auxiliary term by theorists in psychology when no other seems to work. It is currently cropping up with unprecedented frequency in ethology. In natural settings animals display inexplicable and regular deviations from the predictable stimulus-response activity in the laboratory. The phenomena also occur there, though it has generally been rare and anomalous enough to convince researchers that it is nothing more than neurological pathology. Given the artificiality and deprivation of the typical lab cage, they may not be far off the mark.

However, once animal behaviorists began meeting their subjects on their own ground, so to speak, they were forced to expand their ideas about the potentialities of animal consciousness. Apes that use sign language, the sonar and gestural communications of dolphins, elephants' "funeral" processions and handling of deceased relatives' bones—for a long time these and many other instances of humanlike intelligence were known only to ardent naturalists. Had scientists cared or dared to venture into the field more often, perhaps the reports of these facts would not have struck them as so outlandish and questionable. Be that as it may, behavioral scientists are presently owning up to the often narrow expertise of their various disciplines. The progressives among them agree that intelligence and sentience (feeling) are not the monopolies of *Homo sapiens*, but are in fact closely graded in the animal kingdom along a continuum of brain and nervous system complexity.

Any criterion for humanization in ethology and zoology must be based on a "benefit of the doubt" principle. That is, given our vast ignorance of prehuman consciousness, it must be assumed that our closer evolutionary cousins in greater or lesser degrees feel pain and distress (i.e., sundering from social and natural habitat) and, conceivably, varieties of sorrow more psychic than physical. Allowing these, we must logically go on to credit our own species with differing capacities for happiness, fulfillment, bliss, and the possible ecstasy of evolutionary transcendence. If such a rationale seems an impossible idealism, be it remembered that all human civilizations have possessed it in one form or another. Such peoples as the American Indians are our great teachers in this area of humanity.

Mind and consciousness evolve in parallel with biological structure and must be included in any true theory of organic evolution. "Conscious evolution" is therefore a psychophysical process. For needed simplification, we can think of the development of consciousness as a general increasing of awareness. Whether animals can remotely be thought of as having any sense of "self-consciousness" in

the human mode is a provocative question, albeit a moot one for analytic thought. Our inquiry here is necessarily restricted to a consideration of consciousness as the dynamic impetus of *purpose* in evolving
nature. Though this book shares the view of the writers, mentioned
earlier, who view every atomic particle in the universe as alive and
conscious, our main ground of concern from here on will be organismic
consciousness, specifically animal and human. These forms of consciousness are the only ones accessible to deep research, and perhaps
near enough to collective human concern to be deemed practically
relevant.

The theories of transformism (Lamarck-Butler-Bergson) and field
formationism (Hardy-Watson-Sheldrake) between them connect and
support the facts of individual inherited intelligence and what is called
(by Jungians) the "collective unconscious." Both theories, as discussed
in prior chapters, emphasize the import of *new learned behavior* or
experience as the overt clue to evolution. Transformism trains on
genetic memory as the *modus operandi*, while field formationism
offers the morphogenetic field and telepathy as its "contingent
system."

Recognizing that all matter in the universe is organized in some
sort of modular hierarchy at any level of analysis—atomic, cellular,
organismic—a species may be classified as devolved if its state of
awareness and behavior has become fixed, automatic, hyperhabitual,
and uninnovative in its overall environmental coping. Ants and bees
would be examples of such developmental inversion. Though super-
specialization and rigid social cohesion have resulted in their vast
numerical superiority for many millions of years, a peculiar set of
unprecedented changes in the biosphere could potentially decimate
them in a relatively short time. Dinosaurs no doubt exited earth
through the trap-door of inflexibility, along with an eons-long parade of
other known and unknown species.

It is thought by some ethologists and evolutionists that, prior to
reaching the stage of fully stabilized devolution, a species passes
through a phase of optimal evolutionary capacity lasting perhaps several thousands of years. This is the period in which certain individuals
or communities "take the option" to break out of the psychobehavioral
set of the genus and originate a new species or subspecies. Hyper-
awareness and a kind of concerted agitation characterize the initial
impulse. The psychological transformation of consciousness, according to Lamarckians, effects biogenetic transmutation, with structural
and physiological changes manifesting at a later stage.

The transformist logic has it that all evolutionary change comes
about only through the processing of a coordinating agency. The central
nervous system is that agency. In computerlike fashion it "makes

sense" of incoming stimuli, sorting out and dispatching sensory information to organ tissues, cells, and ultimately genes. In the genes it is stored in code for the generations to come.

Hence, the first movements of evolutionary transition are below the surface of obvious behavior, being psychoneurological in essence. The shift of the "break-away" faction may even be invisible to the parent stock. Only after many generations of genetic reconstitution and physical adjustment to the new circumstances opted for, will the structural differences be distinct enough to prompt the specialists to define a new category.

Lamarck and Butler especially saw memory as the motivational secret of evolution, sustaining its continuity. They believed that learned behavior/experience is stored in some bank of memory, and the cumulative legacy—inherited characteristics—is passed on over generations by mechanisms then unknown. And indeed, the latest genetic research indicates that this is precisely what happens: information from the central nervous system is coded at the macromolecular level in RNA and protein. The developing code thus undergoes perpetual revision before feeding back into the gene-bank, where the new design is preserved waiting to be acted upon by its inheritors. The actual reconstitution of structure never ceases, however, providing that each generation maximizes its genetic bequeathal and potential.

The RNA/DNA derepression system is where biogeneticists have begun to truly understand how the chemical controls actually work, activating and deactivating specialized tissue cells so that an entire organ may eventually be reshaped for its new work demands. While all of this is going on the genetic base is relatively plastic, and impermanent or "lingering" modifications are noticeable.

Genetic memory is, then, something more than a hypothetical euphemism. It can be broadly likened to a guidance system, programmed to pilot the organism through the contingencies and demands of its ongoing development. Naturally, if the code is heavily distorted by transmutational error (attributable to bypassed or mistimed choices), the directional blueprint is consequently affected and the organism may slide toward "genetic decay" (coined by Konrad Lorenz) if the subsequent momentum of the negative trait(s) goes uncountered by more creative behavior.

Connecting volition with structural change cannot be done cursorily, occurring as it does through long passages of pangenerational time. Commonsense intelligence can discern the similarities and continuities among diverse species, but the fine lines of species transmutation are traceable only by anthropology, anatomy, and paleontology. Human existence is infant in measure to the temporal immensities involved. This is the reality that renders the crude "creationist" argument against evolution wholly illogical and absurd. If these misled religionists equate the gaps in the fossil record with holes in the logic of the theory itself, they should play fair and apply such "logic" unselectively to their own beliefs and see how it fares as common sense. Suffice it to say that, as a subscience, paleontology is prodigious and promising, and is filling in the fossil gaps as time goes on. Collecting old bones may seem an undramatic way of digging up evidence for evolution, but there is none more substantial.

But in morphogenetics there is something more to go on than old bones. Along with paleontology, anthropology, and experimental genetics, embryogenesis offers up its truly convincing testimony. The developing human embryo, for example, completely transpires in a relatively short time period the multimillion-year development of its race. Ontogeny (individual development) once again recapitulates phylogeny (racial development).

By following the itinerary of the embryo through its full gestation, we are studying evolution *in motion*. It is as if a two-hour reel of film were speeded up to a 30-second clip. In this case the billion-plus years of humankind's evolutionary physical history is played out *in utero* by each of its members before emerging into the light of individuality and singular humanity. An awe-inspiring process that has engirdled the earth and used up epochs is perpetually compressed into a period of nine months and an area no larger than the womb.

Witnessing photographed embryogenesis in any species is an impressive crash course in evolution, but the human version provides the full picture. First, the egg divides into 2 cells, and these subdivide into 4 cells, then 8, 16, 32, and so forth. At last a huge number of cells are contained in a ball, completing this stage known as *cleavage*. *Gastrulation* then proceeds, in which the cleaved cells move about to form three basic tissue layers. These, in systematic and timely sequences, subdivide further and meld into tissues and organs. In the final phase of organ formation, semiautonomous organ systems develop that become wholly functioning entities (kidneys, heart, lungs, brain, etc.). The orchestration of this ontogenetic symphony is a mystery. We see the "music" but have little idea of how the score itself is created.

Research by the reams in embryogenetics has so far failed to solve its double-faceted enigma: How do cells with identical genetic makeup differentiate structurally into specialized tissue groups, and how do these tissue groups find their functional locations in organ formation? From all evidence, the genetic "push" of the first process seems to be accelerated and/or completed by a subtle "pull" that appears to be an amplification in the second. The embryonic organizer has been posited as a master-gene, the regulator of derepression of genes within each cell and, thus, the determinant of its tissual specialization. However, to date such a mechanism has not been isolated and remains a vagary. In its absence a growing number of unconventional theorists are closing ranks with Lyall Watson in considering the existence of "a sort of stream of shared experiences that allows only the best copies of the species plan to survive," a morphological medium that perhaps relays in extradimensional elaborations of the DNA instructional code. States Watson, "Telepathy could do this."[1]

Watson's use of the qualifier *could* reflects a skepticism that is the historical attitude in science. For much too long have scientists considered paranormal phenomena best left to spiritualists and other traders in the occult. These latter, delighted with the bargain, have spirited away (for money) most objective thought on the subject. Happily, it is gradually being recovered by the initiative of the New Physics and the advent of sophisticated technologies. Professor Burr, in his long, arduous detective work with L-fields, brought the subject of telepathy closer to reality. Like most researchers, he avoided use of that bias-laden word, and rightly so, since during his career it was stock occult. Today it is being restored to common sense, with some help from the lab.

The fact that morphogenetic fields exist in the womb during embryogenesis is substantiation for the operation of telepathiclike fields on the larger scale. Hardy's idea of "psychic blueprinting" takes on a more solid meaning when its effects are recorded step by step. The irony is that its ethereal nature is precisely what induces unbelief in the strict materialists, until new methods enable it to be seen or measured. Useful as it is as a limited experimental principle, "seeing" is not always "believing." The naked eye is not a wanton deceiver, but the mind behind it frequently is.

In his standard text *Patterns and Principles of Animal Development*, John W. Saunders, Jr., states, "The [morphogenetic] field properties extend beyond the limits of the tissue that actually contributes to the construction of the specific organ" (italics in the original).[2] Thus, the epidermis being the outermost organ, we have an electrodynamic continuum from ovule to organismic "aura." Various individuals, today known as "sensitives," have since time immemorial reported their visions of these auras and often were ridiculed or burned at the stake for their trouble. In more enlightened societies they were sometimes commonplace, as plentiful as doctors and psychiatrists in our own, whose healing functions they antedated.

Morphogenetic researchers have been slow to refer to L-fields as electrodynamic, although this is the obvious conclusion. Perhaps they would rather avoid aping the concepts of physics—understandable enough. On the other hand, morphogenetic theory is not long out of the laboratory, and the most apropos terminology should be used without reserve.

The celebrated cross-disciplinarian and inventor R. Buckminster Fuller has had no qualms about borrowing wholesale from technical physics in setting forth his elaborate rendition of the modular universe. Here is a sample of his *Synergetics*:

> Universe is the comprehensive, historically synchronous, integral-aggregate system embracing the integral-aggregate systems of all men's consciously apprehended and communicated (to self and others) nonsimultaneous, nonidentical, but always complementary and only partially overlapping, macro-micro, always-and-every-where, omnitransforming, physical and metaphysical, weighable and unweighable event sequences. Universe is a dynamically synchronous scenario that is unitarily nonconceptual as of any one moment, yet as an aggregate of finities is sum-totally finite.[3]

These are only the first strokes of the whole sketch. Fuller continues:

> Energy can neither be created or lost; therefore it is finite. Thus, man has been able to define successfully physical Universe—but not, as yet, the metaphysical Universe.... The total of experiences is integrally synergetic. Universe is the comprehensive a priori synergetic integral.... Angle and frequency modulations, either subjective or objective in respect to man's consciousness, discretely define all experiences which altogether constitute Universe.[4]

Idiomatic extravagance for the mass market was never before pressed into service like this. Only a popular genius with large thoughts is sanctioned to speak in the kind of cryptic convolution that usually weighs down the pages of academic treatises. But Fuller is among other things a scientific philosopher, and he is using the technologese alone capable of carrying his ideas, mathematical in this case. His is an electrodynamic description of the cosmos, vibrant and "bursting out all over." Being symbological, it is not readily visualized—the reader is left to form his own image of it. And that construct will not likely be very different from the Web of Life or *élan vital*. Fuller does drop a familiar metaphor, however, a nicely visual supplement to his model:

> In the endless but finite and never exactly repeating (Heisenberged) "film-strip" scenario of evolutionary Universe, after the film strip has been projected it goes through a dissolved phase and re-forms again to receive the ever-lastest self-intertransforming patterning just before being again projected.[5]

A film-strip like no other, this, without end yet finite, ceaselessly reeling out a flux of events, no two "frames" of which are ever precisely the same. Temporal, physical possibilities are played out in the projection-light of consciousness, and are at length dissolved for new potentiality in the "darkroom" of subconsciousness. So the physical alternates interminably with the metaphysical, and the salient result is ever-increasing complexity and refinement of the synergetic universe.

Beyond saying that mind is the projector of the cosmic event, we can pursue the metaphor no further. The notion itself is a finite one, though it should be added that Fuller's universe-film is most accurately conceived as projected in or over a sphere. His geodesic dome would be an appropriate world-screen from the terrestrial viewpoint. Though the saucer is inverted from our perspective, we are discovering its transparency and penetrableness, and the fact that its prime limitation is illusion. And as in any earthly movie, its aesthetics can be enjoyed. Make no mistake, this one is alive and jumping. If the viewer-participant falls asleep in the showing, it is because his eyes and mind were half-closed when he came in.

Evolutionary schemes of wide variety can be drawn up from all the branches of science. Each will be incomplete at the limits of its knowledge, though this alone does not invalidate it. Only when broad-spectrumed insight is lacking will it remain merely a scheme, and most likely a misleading one.

The idiom of physics has been preferred among many evolutionists outside of biology because it defines material boundaries that encompass the nominally biological. Obviously, it deals with the largest and the smallest known spheres of possible evolution, this side of the metaphysical. The discovery of relativistic realities, for example, has helped greatly to expand the general framework by dispelling naively absolutist outlooks on time and space. At the macro fringe of the observable universe we see galaxies in accelerating migration to parts unknown.

Heisenberg's Principle of Uncertainty (indeterminacy) has proven that the world is essentially open on the hypomicro, subatomic end and is irrevocably altered when probed with micro methods (electron microscopes, etc.), the only ones in our possession. In the shape of the ballooning mushroom, the psyche-chilling instance of the unseen world erupts into the visible. So nuclear physics has ominously revised the meaning of "seeing is believing."

In an appendix titled "Physicists and Mystics: Similarities in World View," from a book by Lawrence LeShan,[6] the author reveals how the description of the universe by modern theoretical physicists and serious mystics is oftentimes virtually indistinguishable. A quote from, say, Buddha is eerily comparable to one from Max Planck. More and more, the findings of modern physics are suggesting processes we would ordinarily associate with the workings of consciousness. This has led other writers, such as Theodore Roszak, to speculate that the greater "patterns and purposes" of design in the universe are more fundamental than its singular coordinates and dynamics and that "mentality is the basic, irreducible continuum of the universe." He asks, "What, then, if the mechanistic model of reality is exactly the inverse of the truth?"[7]

The inevitable conclusion is that mind (the ultimate form of it) originates matter, and matter is illusional in that it is substantiated only by relative forms of consciousness, derived from mind. The fact is stated briefly by University of Paris professor of physics Bernard d'Espagnat: "The doctrine that the world is made up of objects whose existence is independent of human consciousness turns out to be in conflict with quantum mechanics and the facts established by experiment."[8]

And Sir Arthur Eddington said it in even fewer words—"The stuff of the world is mind-stuff." That mind-stuff is molded to form in conscious evolution.

Chapter Fifteen

MIND AND METAMORPHOSIS

For which cause we faint not; but though our outward man perish, yet the inward man is renewed day by day.

2 Corinthians 4:16

In writing on an immensity such as evolution, it is tempting to try for a sweeping overview at the end to tie together all the relevant threads and perhaps achieve a grand finale in the bargain. But that impulse is more a habit of Western aesthetics than a requirement of format. There are many excellent volumes (some listed in the bibliography) that capture large portions of the evolutionary panorama quite well from various perspectives. It is hoped that the reader will have found the present one beneficial in its own right, as a sizable area of ground was taken in from both the micro and macro poles. The broad scope was needed to travel across a vastly changing landscape of thought and theory. Any attempt to glorify in our conclusion a subject that is already larger than life would be anticlimactic to this, the greatest of cosmic dramas.

Majesty includes things that are often taken for granted. And what do we humans take for granted more than ourselves? Although the sea is the sea, one of the stages in its own evolution was the formation of raindrops from vapor. Too often we think of the cosmos as that overawing, star-strewn void "out there," forgetting that each of us is a modular universe made of the same star-stuff, as science popularizers are wont to point out. Our bodies teem with multitudinous, microscopic life that may be far more sentient than we have heretofore considered. Usually it is only when these minuscule beings threaten our health that we experience their *élan* and, perhaps, relate them to our mind and behavior. We see something like the same effect in the ills of society. Problems are acknowledged only after violence erupts, and still many people point to the unpleasantness "out there." But the cosmos is, literally, under our very nose.

Mystics of all traditions have been reminding their fellow humans of this profound truth ever since they gained the time to stop and listen. Thus the idea of the modular universe is not a modern insight; it is at least as old as culture itself. On the other hand, as history testifies, humankind has always demonstrated an inveterate tendency to forget such central truths. And so forgetfulness holds back the evolution of individuals. As Butler and the neo-Lamarckians hold, the terrestrial process is grounded in the need to rise above existing levels, individually and collectively, and to remember the ground that has been gained, which is the base camp to future heights.

It is no surprise, then, that remembrance or recollection is fundamental in esoteric-mystical disciplines. The outward forms are usually meditation, contemplation, litany, and so on. What may be less familiar is that the authentic systems are dedicated to nothing other than the developmental destiny of the human—evolution. The aim is movement into ever greater reality. But the evidence of success in the project is not always on public display—that is, the uncommonly achieving, socially integrated, and well-rounded human. Any practice(s) unproductive of this end will tend to result in the inverse.

Bogus systems aplenty achieve this effect, specializing in little else than salable sanctimony and social stimulation under the guise of spirituality. At best they dose their supporters with innocuous illusion, at worst addict them to dangerous delusions. Of such stuff are gurus and bloody Jonestowns made.

For the most part, however, cults and pseudocults merely recycle and veneer a set of pervasive psychic symptoms, surpassingly described by R. Buckminster Fuller:

> Typical of the "games" played by man which preclude his timely recognition of the fundamentals of evolution are: vision-blinding national and local eccentricities; obsessions with legendary "perfections" of yesterday; preoccupation with murder and scandal news; molelike shortsightedness developed by constant attention to before-the-nose successive personal and local crises and ambitions; narrowness of focus due to specialization; pride, inferiority complex; and spring fever.[1]

When one's chuckle fades after the last turn of Fuller's incision, the depth of it begins to sink in. The scope of this syndrome takes in all of us, save the "Complete Man"—one name for those developed individuals who have taken on the onus of higher consciousness and human evolution. But these latter terms are so accreted with mental and emotional baggage that the substance behind them is semifictional to the ordinary person. Distracted as the average person is by those "games" Fuller enumerates, he is not likely to recognize the Complete Man should he be fortunate enough to meet him, because the Complete Man himself will probably be ordinary in externals. Though a part of his reality is in "legendary 'perfections' of yesterday," his essence must be sought and developed in living forms. To relegate him to scripture, history, or myth is to exile him from all personal relevance; for the Complete Man is the real Self in all of us, waiting to be evolved.

Modern society is one gone sour on traditional ideals, while yet searching the meaning and value in life. The search has become desperate. The cultural atmosphere is polluted with political poisons and interpersonal *angst*. "The world is out of joint" to a magnitude that would have amazed the author of that expression, William Shakespeare. A Complete Man of the first order, with a complete handle on the human condition, he was not alone in seeing and feeling the developing dilemma of civilization, especially as manifesting in the West. Today he would find company everywhere, for more and more people are realizing, in Arthur Deikman's words, that

> something is wrong. I've noticed it for a long time, as if there is something odd or unreal about the world. Most of the time I'm busy

with what I'm doing and don't notice, but, sooner or later, that persistent nagging awareness emerges again, telling me that something is peculiar about my view of things, and everyone else's, too.

I don't mean that the world seems to be collapsing—starvation, atomic bombs, pollution—it isn't just those things, drastic as they may be. There is something still more basically wrong. It's as if you went to the movies and there was something odd about the projector or something strange about the camera that was used to take the movies in the first place. The images themselves seem normal, but the way it is put together is out of sequence, or taken at different speeds, or the perspective keeps changing....There is something basically wrong with the structure of the world—as we have been taught to see it—but you might not notice it for a long while....

Time makes no sense. It really doesn't apply to me; it doesn't fit ... inside you're like some kind of mirror, reflecting everything without absorbing it. The mirror doesn't change. You watch time pass ... but it really doesn't fit that clear place inside. Time fits my body and the world I see, but it doesn't fit me.[2]

The disruption or diversion of one's perceptual stream and the sense that time is out of control is, of course, precisely what Shakespeare was talking about. But where these were once voiced only in the jeremiads of sensitive poets and philosophers, they are the basis today of mass complaints being laid in the laps of doctors and psychiatrists all over the world. The foregoing account is by a psychiatrist who is also a distinguished writer. In his book, he begins his discussion of the crisis with the cybernetic metaphor of consciousness-as-filmstrip, where we left off in our last chapter. He diagnoses the malfunction in the "filmstrip's" projection as a desynchronization of the active and receptive modes of awareness and prescribes certain meditative and contemplative attitudes (highly developed in the Orient) to restore the lost harmony between mind and body. Then reality can be registered and focused more toward personal sanity.

There are many ways to talk about the consciousness crisis; its distortions are transpersonal, refracting through all the spheres of human experience, past and present, and projecting into the future. But the felt fragmentation of Self finds ready expression in the bad-movie analogy. Its imagery seems to intimate the very drive of neo-Lamarckian dynamics—need, continuity, memory.

According to the Fullerian, "Heisenbergered" idea of the universal, evolutionary "filmstrip," individuated points of consciousness can be understood as space-time coordinates. These are complexed and patterned in "aggregate-systems" that are projected as symmetry, constituting the multimodular (micro-macro) universe. Synergy, in a sense, is activated "mind-stuff," the primordial *élan vital* out of which is structured the formal cosmos; hydrogen appears to be its first material manifestation after light and energy radiation. As touched upon in previous chapters, "worlds within worlds" are organized both laterally and vertically (hierarchically) in spherical, non-Euclidian space. Thus, our cosmic film could be picturesquely entitled The Great Web of Life, and accurately so, if everything in it is indeed alive.

Such a conceptual construct can only hint at the real structure. There are a number of comprehensive and detailed models, one of the more metaphysically polished being P. D. Ouspensky's *A New Model of the Universe*. Other, equally valid versions have been cited herein, but central to most is the theme of the hologram, where the whole is reflected in the part, macro in micro, and vice versa. Here it is fitting to reintroduce the brain-as-transformer, outlining its directive role in terrestrial evolution.

Like the planet on which it is evolving, the human brain is a globular marvel of electrodynamic organization. The superstructure in both (earth's biosphere, brain's neocortex) is the outgrowth of vertical development. Just as the ecocrust of the earth was the last formed in geologic succession, so the cerebral cortex is the latest and outermost formation of the mammalian cognitive organ, the human thinking cap. As the most highly evolved on earth, the neomammalian brain is a repository of sorts of all earth history. The vaster portion of that registered history would, of course, be buried at subconscious levels.

The brain and the spinal cord together constitute the central nervous system. Its verticality in humans is a recent innovation in morphological time, and this "brains-up" posture is symbolic of humankind's high aspiration, as has been widely and richly appreciated. However, there must be much more function than symbol involved in *Homo sapiens'* design, not only in terms of his extraterrestrial concerns but also in the work he must yet do in reprogramming himself from earth-exploiter to earth-keeper. His manipulative powers must now be used to restore health to the natural environment he has disequilibrized with his upright arrogance and aggression. Lest we condemn our species too much, however, we should remember that much of its imperfection is simply that of immaturity—narcissism, impatience, lack of vision—and may be rectified by guided maturation. There is evidence for new beginnings. It is seen in the newly emergent interest in preserving the natural environment, prevention of nuclear war, and growing disillusionment with materialistic values.

Two-legged activities such as hunting, food gathering, and later fire tending were first paid for by protoman with pressure and stress on his CNS. He was molded into a "bundle of nerves" by his very survival agenda. Excess of aggression had nowhere to go but up through his verticalized spinal column, and this energy had to be accommodated and diffused in an enlarged brain. There his aggression was refined into ambition in the biochemistry of cognition. He became a calculative creature, growing ever more aware of his cerebral prowess and the uses to which he could put it.

As clever as humankind's cogitations became, still he was driven by the libidinal energy of his lower centers. He became a physical paradox. Establishing his lordship over the plant and animal kingdoms, as well as his fellow human, he arduously learned the principles of material causality. He became an inventor and producer. On his neo-mammalian brain he rose to culture. He perceived patterns in the workings of all the world around him—but locally and discontinuously. His individuated identity was a given of his social function within the clan or tribe. Community provided sanctuary from the inner and outer terrors of aloneness, but in most cases it did not endow its members with the knowledge and fortitude necessary for the inevitable confrontation with the origin of those terrors: separation from their universal and real Self. Society was therefore a double-edged sword that warded off the greater threats of nature, "red in tooth and claw," while yet was turned by the species upon itself in personal conflict and group warfare. Even as their *élan vital* roiled ceaselessly in the pressurization of id and ego, humans continued to look upward and outward for the meaning of it all. The stars gave the glimmer of an answer. Astrologer-priests were the first formally to seek inner and outer connections.

The rise and spread of civilization followed the structural expansion of the bilateral brain. For the brain had evolved as two-in-one within the cranium, like Siamese twins in the womb. Both functioned to integrate and synthesize ever-widening ranges of experience and to organize it into meaningful wholes.

Although modern brain research lauds itself at its discovery of the bimodal brain and its parallel division of labor—intellect and intuition—it is most curious that a precedent for this understanding was clearly established as early as 1911 by the advocate of creative evolution, Henri Bergson. Putting the question of bimodal consciousness within the context of evolution, Bergson writes,

> In the course of ... evolution, while some beings have fallen more and more asleep, others have more and more completely awakened, and the torpor of some has served the activity of others. But the waking could be effected in two different ways. Life, that is to say consciousness launched into matter, fixed its attention either on its own movement or on the matter it was passing through; and it has thus been turned either in the direction of intuition or in that of intellect. Intuition, at first sight, seems far preferable to intellect, since in it life and consciousness remain within themselves....

From this point of view, not only does consciousness appear as the motive principle of evolution, but also, among conscious beings themselves, man comes to occupy a privileged place.[3]

The beauty of Bergson's notion of creative evolution is that it accommodates both the physical and the metaphysical (consciousness). In fact, as the above passage attests, he considers consciousness the more fundamental (the "motive principle") in the total evolutionary process. His identification of the intellect with the physical or material and intuition with the metaphysical or spiritual ("life and consciousness") is interesting indeed. His position on the primacy of intuition is clearly in agreement with certain contemporary brain researchers, such as Dr. Ornstein, who emphasize that intuition, or right-brain development, is an essential step in the development of expanded consciousness, and thus a step to higher human evolution.

Anyone who has browsed oriental philosophy knows that the polar nature of the human psyche is anything but new knowledge. The various cosmologies revolve, in fact, on the idea of complementary dualism at all levels of the universe. The ultimate polarity in the manifest world is macro-micro, or the one and the many, unity and diversity, and so forth. Beyond that is Being and Nothing (Void). Perhaps the most familiar aspect of this first ontological principle, however, is that of the male-female in the life process. Almost everyone has seen some variation of the yin-yang symbol of Taoism:

But one does not have to wing through blue-sky metaphysics to grasp the broad implications of bimodal consciousness in human evolution. They are observable in each of us, although in our hyped-up modern culture one of the "Siamese twins" has traditionally been a social outcast; it is the receptive and contemplative self. For a people who believe that doing anything is better than doing nothing, its qualities are felt to be unworthy of cultivation. Consider this account from the writer who gave us the bad-movie metaphor:

> As conscious doing is the essence of the action mode, allowing is the essence of the receptive. With the action mode we divide and conquer our environment. With the receptive, we take in, receive and unify. It is the difference between breathing out and breathing

in. Try a sample now. Take a full breath; breathe in and then breathe out. Notice the difference in your state of mind during those two phases. On inhaling, mental contents become diffuse, thinking tends to stop.

On exhaling, energy flows out, the vision sharpens; thinking, too, is sharper on exhalation, boundaries more clear.[4]

Let's be a little clearer about the physiological facet of the consciousness crisis. It is an unbalance or desynchronization of the appositional brain and/or mind. The "bad movie" is out-of-sync primarily in the perceptions of its viewers and, secondarily—but no less actually—in the warped structures of the outer world. The outer is reflected in the inner. The movie-goer watches The Enchanted Loom, but he is also living in and altering it at the same time. The universal film is in reality the whole of life itself, and individual projections of it are, so to speak, integral pieces of footage in it. With the active mode of consciousness we shoot our footage, with the receptive we watch. Most of the film-making between involves alternations of the two. It can truthfully be said without tongue in cheek that, having made our movie, we must live in it.

The vast phenomena of evolution cannot be encompassed by any analogy, however. Language itself is but a "figure of speech," essential as it is for our social existence. Cosmologies are the greatest of metaphors that intimate ontological ultimates, including the *becoming* of evolution. It is the manifestation process of the potential forms of macrocosmic *being*.

Looking again at the yin-yang circle, we can see how it describes the expansion-contraction (active-receptive) cycles of any life form when it is ideally balanced. The locus of the curve signifies the integration of the two hemispheres. On a sphere the locus connects the poles in a continuum that is in-turning and out-turning in apposition. The visualization is enhanced when the sphere is revolving. The similarity to earth with its roughly parallel curvature of sea and continents is obviously striking.

In an expanding universe such as ours, it is reasonable to speculate that each module, or being, has the conscious capacity to regulate the dynamics of its own expansion and contraction in an overall pattern of unfoldment. In healthy forms this would be the correct balance of inner and outer factors in dual complement. In unhealthy ones the opposite would obtain; contraction accelerates in imbalance, with disease and death making their appearance before the being has achieved its full potential in harmony with the greater cosmos. This is the essence of oriental philosophy, be it expressed in Taoism, Zen Buddhism, Hinduism, Sufism, or even in Christian or Jewish Mysticism, or any valid hybrid thereof. These traditions contain self-development methodologies that are sciences of the highest order. Correctly practiced, they metamorphose the unfulfilled person with capacity into the Complete, Universal Person. Forerunners of this fulfilled human have been the transcendent figures and founders of religion and all creative human enterprises. A list of these is not required, though. The publicly revered ones are far outnumbered by the unknown. In this realm it is the function, not the form, that matters.

Early on it was noted how the scientific paradigm or "overriding theoretical framework" was useful in guiding research and rendering data meaningful. At the same time, the high propensity of a paradigm to become habitualized and institutionalized was also stressed. In layman's terms a *paradigm* is simply an established perspective that offers a direction for further exploration. If a paradigm begins too narrow in scope or becomes reductive as it gains momentum, it will increase conceptual inertia, to cast the problem in the terms of physics. The paradigm becomes a *paradigm fixé*; insights and possibilities that do not fit handily into its closed frame will be ignored or discarded.

In another section tautologies—circular arguments—were shown to be the final deterioration of theories that remain bound to *paradigm fixé*. Tautologies abound everywhere, in all fields of thought. They "prove" themselves by never leaving the premises on which they begin; their plane of logic is fixed. And since modern physics tells us that space and time are curved, and all events therein, the supposition is warranted that a singular idea will inevitably close upon itself as an *idée fixé* if it never leaves the plane on which it was born.

Thus, there are some deformed concepts of the Future Human floating around. Crawl inside this one and get the feel of it:

> Perhaps some day it will be possible to add a variety of cognitive and intellectual prosthetic devices to the brain—a kind of eyeglasses for the mind. This would be in the spirit of the past accretionary evolution of the brain and is probably far more feasible than attempting to restructure the existing brain. Perhaps we will one day have surgically implanted in our brains small replaceable computer modules or radio terminals which will provide us with a rapid and fluent knowledge of Basque, Urdu, Amharic, Ainu, Albanian, Nu, Hopi, Kung, or Delphinese; or numerical values of the incomplete gamma function and the Tschebysheff polynomials; or the natural history of animal spoor; or all legal precedents for the ownership of floating islands; or radio telepathy connecting several human beings, at least temporarily, in a form of symbiotic association previously unknown to our species.[5]

Though this sounds like a runaway cartoon, it comes from a serious popularizer of science. From all appearances he is a level-headed enthusiast of what technology has to offer. But this nonsensical mix of cybernetical fantasies is presented as an evolutionary prospectus. It has almost nothing to do with evolution in the primary sense: the development of mind and body in nature. This is mere accessorizing of the existing form, and the fact that the author drops the phrase "accretionary evolution" (whatever that means) into the surreal scenario gives away his confusion of what the phenomenon actually is. Evidently spring fever can strike earnest rationalists, even as they write. What is more amazing is that there are a number of widely read publicists sincerely presenting the same kind of pictures of this "homo prostheticus."

Robotic versions of human advancement are the progeny of the 20th-century materialistic *Zeitgeist*. They are self-fulfilling prophecies of the *paradigm fixé* in Western science. As such they are the epiphenomenal proof of the possibility of human *devolution*. Of course, highly developed technologies are an essential, if peripheral, part of human progress, especially as aids in mundane earth tasks and future space colonization. But the mass obsession with things mechanical goes far beyond necessity, even of the normal need of humans for object manipulation. Gadgetry knows no bounds in Western society. In the health sciences it tends to replace perception and intuition with computer printouts in diagnosis and treatment. The prosthesis is undeniably a godsend for the physically handicapped; but the mechanistic approach pervading "internal" medicine may be disabling more people than it is helping. There is a wealth of enlightening literature on this problem.*

The reader may have noticed by now that no mention has been made thus far of the latest breakthrough in applied biology—genetic engineering. This project is sometimes referred to as "shaping life in the lab," thereby implying the templating of organismic forms. The phrase is misleading because, like prostheses, the manipulations involved are *after the fact*, that is, after the primary form of the organism has evolved. Procedures such as gene-splicing and cloning alter and replicate established structures but do not generate or shape forms in anything like a holistic mode. The work itself is intriguing and has impressive potential in the fields of immunology and, for example, the artificial synthesis of new energy fuels. Yet again, this technology may be misapplied like any other in a culture given to tinkering.**

Though the reductionistic method has produced a large theoretical and practical yield in biology, there are clear dangers. In *The Turning Point*, Fritjof Capra underscores the gravest one:

---

*See Annotation, "The Future Human."
**See Annotation, "Bioengineering and Evolution."

In biology the Cartesian view of living organisms as machines, constructed from separate parts, still provides the dominant conceptual framework. Although Descartes' simple mechanistic biology could not be carried very far and had to be modified considerably during the subsequent three hundred years, the belief that all aspects of living organisms can be understood by reducing them to their smallest constituents, and by studying the mechanisms through which these interact, lies at the very basis of most contemporary biological thinking....

Carried away by the successes of the reductionist method, most notably recently in the field of genetic engineering, they tend to believe that it is the only valid approach, and they have organized biological research accordingly....Consequently biologists have developed very curious ways of dealing with living organisms.[6]

This holds as well for many of our institutions. In prisons and mental hospitals shock overcomes curiosity in first-time visitors, and they often appear more disturbed than the residents. Nursing homes are notorious as abodes of atrophy.

Even schools are lit more with tension and anxiety than happy learning. And it is here, in compulsory Western education, that most critics say that the consciousness crisis gets under way in all seriousness. One of these, Marilyn Ferguson, set down the crux of it in *The Aquarian Conspiracy*.

As the greatest single social influence during the formative years, schools have been the instruments of our greatest denial, unconsciousness, conformity, and broken connections. Just as allopathic medicine treats symptoms without concern for the whole system, schools break knowledge and experience into "subjects," relentlessly turning wholes into parts, flowers into petals, history into events, without ever restoring continuity....

Worst yet, not only the mind is broken, but too often, so is the spirit. Allopathic teaching produces the equivalent of *iatrogenic*, or "doctor-caused" illness—teacher-caused learning disabilities. We might call these *pedogenic* illnesses. The child who may have come to school intact, with the budding courage to risk and explore, finds stress enough to permanently diminish that adventure.[7]

Unconsciousness, broken connections, broken spirit ... *élan vital* escapes the system and its very lust for life is lost. Contraction and devolution set in subtly and slowly, and the tragedy is that it is taken for normality—so many people are doing it.

At this juncture a distinction between *involution* and *devolution* should be made. Some writers use the two terms interchangeably in describing retrograde process or degeneration, the opposite of evolution. However, the present usage of *involution* implies rather the receptive complement of the psyche, as given in the yin-yang dynamic. It is the in-folding of the curve or locus. In that context it would be involvement within, interior movement, balanced by outer action-unfolding. In imbalance the two together would shift into retrograde devolution, common on the terrestrial plane.

Traditional classroom education contributes to mental devolution by overconditioning left-hemisphere capacities to the detriment of the right. Studies that call on sequential, calculative abilities are pressed upon all students, regardless of interest or aptitude. "Math anxiety" is carried over into the sciences and even some humanities, such as English and history. The arts (music, dance, painting, etc.) are perceived as not much more than recreations, diversions from the "real studies," rather than precious means in themselves of learning about the real world. And since these activities are integrative, allowing participants to experience their bodies and the environment in wholes, they register much more personal relevance for those whose minds are not disposed to rationalization and rote skills. Both kinds of cognition are necessary for healthy mentation, but to force them upon anyone may be one of the surest, though roundabout, ways of getting nonconformists from schools into prisons and psychiatric wards. On this authorities assuredly agree.

More and more educators contend that the way to quit miseducating people is to first get them out of the straitjacket of the conventional teacher-pupil or sage-and-fools caste system. They maintain that the arbiter of learning and higher knowledge is experience, not the dispensers of information that we call "teachers." Though the latter are quite necessary as guides or channels in learning to live creatively in the world, their present roles as classroom masters are more like wardens, more concerned with keeping their charges in line than with enabling them to live more fully.

When positivistic/behavioristic scientists dispensed with the idea of consciousness altogether, art and science became alienated disciplines. The "educated" mind was a split one. At last consciousness is being brought back into science, if reluctantly. Among other advances, enlightened educators are getting people to think about the possibilities of subconscious, osmotic learning. For it may have shaped our society and our lives more than most of us ever know. It is on subconscious levels that we may have to relearn the universe and our role in it. As a species we have yet to learn our destiny. That destiny is tasted in the very task of human evolution. It is nothing less than the transmutation of consciousness toward perfection.

In Zen Buddhism, Sufism, and other mystical currents in East and West, we find the recurring image of metamorphosis: birth, death, and rebirth. This finds vivid expression in the butterfly emerging from the chrysalis. In like manner, human consciousness gives broad evidence of straining to break through to a new collective level. The chrysalis or the protective casing is composed of the lower centers (ego and libidinal layers) that once protected the person. Now this shell is in a quite real sense a barrier that must be breached. The Complete Human is that person who has achieved this transformation and is able to help others with the same task. The present stage may be a markedly difficult one to transcend, hardened as it is by pervasive cultural conditionings. Like a fetus in the labors of the womb, there is much discomfort, even suffering in the transition of humankind to a new state. But unlike much of existence after that first birth, the latter is a movement into rarefied fulfillment and joy. Before that, say the Sufis, "Mankind sleeps in a nightmare of unfulfillment."

As humanity moves up and out into the universe, it will carry the qualities of its consciousness with it. With these it willl seed new forms and propagate existing ones. For better or worse, it has been doing this on earth to a degree far outstripping that of other species. The stewardship of earth is in our hands. In the future, that of other planets will be also. It could well be that the human mind has actually reached the capacity to affect evolutionary dynamics at all points and levels by activating localized electricity (L-fields) with its psychic energy (Thought-fields), which in turn may alter the shape-properties of morphogenetic fields (Sheldrake's "fields of causative formation"). Physicists are beginning to take telepathy seriously. Quantum energy may be diffused as thought-energy. Far from being a mere flight of fantasy, this is probably the everyday way the modular cosmos works, and right under our very nose.

The metamorphic postulate is highly developed in the major cosmologies. This takes the form of a spiritual ascension from what one prominent evolutionist calls "The Ground Unconscious" to Superconsciousness, or God-Consciousness on the uppermost plane.[8] There are very definite (according to their masters) stages in this ascension, and the median number of these in the various traditions is seven. In Sufism, for example, "Seven Men" correspond to the same number of development levels, starting at the lowest level with the depraved, commanding ego-Self and slowly progressing to other stages, such as the "inspired Self," the "fulfilled Self," and so on, and ultimately to the purified and "complete Self."

These ascending levels have been variously described as "degrees in the transmutation of consciousness," and they are ascertained by objectively defined attributes, states, and capacities.

According to the Sufis, development to higher stages does not just happen; it requires special efforts, carried out at the right time, in the right company, with right guidance.

Right guidance may include a definite "course" of study and activity under the direct or indirect guidance of a teacher, one who has already traveled the path: a Complete Man. The Sufis hold that human evolution is something that unfolds under the influence of terrestrial and cosmic laws, and has implications that even transcend such laws. They view so-called "peak experiences" as phenomena occurring at about stage two (out of the total seven). It is there that the organs of higher evolution are in embryo.

Rapprochement with divine knowledge and origin is the inextinguishable desire that casts the illumination of cosmology. In the West such mystical philosophers as Johann Goethe and Pierre Teilhard de Chardin understood love as the life force that draws the human soul to knowledge and reunion with its origin. Divine will or grace, they believed, is the intervention of God in the life of his creation. It is received in the refinement of a higher magnitude at each succeeding level of ascension. Therefore, according to these thinkers, evolution is the dynamic whereby human aspiration is transmuted into God-knowledge and love. The alchemical analogy is one description of the process.

Throughout the course of this book both neo-Darwinist evolutionism and its animated opponent "creationism" have been taken to task. Neo-Lamarckian ideas have been reintroduced as a rectification of their shortcomings, not a complete replacement for them. Lamarck himself never pushed his theory as an *Eureka!* explanation of the whole of evolution or creation. That was more a tendency of the disciples of Darwin, as well as present-day creationists. In polar ways both are reductionist, and their clash was perhaps inevitable from the start. Only a holistic mode of evolutionary understanding can transcend and reconcile them; such is found in undiluted cosmologies. Neo-Lamarckism and Bergson's theory of creative evolution can help heal the rift intellectually. For neither the Darwinists nor the religious fundamentalists are barren of truth, however much they may obscure it.

The faith in a Creator who issued forth his creation as the world has always been found in minds of the highest order of intelligence. These minds have never denied the cosmic logic of evolution. Moses, Jesus, Mohammed, Buddha, and others never condemned a broadmindedness that would not deny out of hand the possibility of evolutionary ascent. They were concerned with transmuting the lower bases of human nature and elevating humanity. And if God indeed works in mysterious ways, why does he not do so in perpetual transformation of species?

On the other hand, neo-Darwinism has collected but misinterpreted a great deal of potentially enlightening data by fixating it upon certain tautologies that superficially and automatically exclude neo-Lamarckian factors such as purpose, design, and transcendental need. Instead, it stumbles about in the insubstantialities of random mutation, extrapolations of probability laws (fortuity), and an inability to look beyond the gene. However, in adaptation it may make a fruitful connection to neo-Lamarckian thought, if only as a minor corollary. Providing it will admit to an evolutionary consciousness, ultra-Darwinism could throw some light on this otherwise dim principle.

The paradigm has shifted, and there is a near possibility of opening the door on a larger and better one. Here is a modern Darwinist who has glimpsed what lies over the horizon of the old one:

> We know a lot, and in some biomathematical detail, about the evolution of individual species on the earth, but no Darwin has yet emerged to take account of the orderly, coordinated growth and differentiation of the whole spectacular System, much less its seemingly permanent survival....
>
> Our part in the world is unfathomable because we have not learned enough, but it is surely not absurd. We have some kind of importance here, for all our bewilderment. We are a significant part of the System. What we do with ourselves, and with the rest of life, makes a difference.[9]

Perhaps higher human consciousness is all that is lacking in today's world. Devolution may be what happens in its absence. The call to higher consciousness that perceives design finds a voice in Rumi, the 13th-century sage: "Because of necessity, man acquires organs. So, necessitous one, increase your need."

Chapter Sixteen

EVOLUTIONARY PERFECTION

The total achievement of science hitherto is but a recognition of a small fraction of the creative thoughts by which the world is made.

Ehrenfried Pfeiffer

Many readers are familiar with Plato's Theory of Forms, a pinnacle of classical Greek thought. It is often held up today as an unexcelled model of Western ratiocination, although the mode of insight that created it is in essence no more Western than Eastern, as much intuitive as logical. As with much metaphysical philosophy, it has been kicked upstairs to the status of abstract idealism, with little relevance to the actual contingencies of here-and-now—that is to say, of material reality. With the advent of modern epistemological theories (e.g., Locke, Kant, Hume) and scientific philosophy in the 18th and 19th centuries, the Theory of Forms was relegated to the teleological museum. It was pretty to contemplate for a few moments, but too far removed from the concreteness and, therefore, "realness" of human existence to be anything more than an antique of ancient cerebralism.

There is, however, no evidence that Plato himself denigrated the input of the senses or regarded them as underminers of truth, as did later European philosophers. On the contrary, he emphasized in *The Republic* that the things of the mind could be reached only through the things of sense. But he also states that the intellectual is more real than the sensual. Plato is saying, then, that human knowledge progresses from the sensate/informational to the cognitive/intellectual. Knowledge increases along a continuum of experience to ever higher wisdom and truth. By *intellect* Plato is not implying only the rationalizing process but primarily the higher perceptual faculty that reflects (as in his allegory "The Cave") greater or lesser (more illusory) degrees of reality.

Represented by the simple figure of the pyramid, the Theory of Forms helps us to understand the progressional relationship between consciousness and morphology in evolution. First we must restate the proposition of an immaterial, supraformal Universal Mind, the transcendent reality that emanates "mind-stuff" into dimensionality, creating the world of substance and particular forms. According to Plato, each individual form, organic or inorganic, is an imperfect reflection of an immutable (or archetypal) Ideal Form beyond space and time, toward which it is impelled.

Thus, starting at the apex of the pyramid, we can analogize the structure as a hierarchy of form, each level of which is of an integration and holization superior to the level(s) below it. In this model, the base represents the form in its greatest particularization, fragmentation, and incompletion. Plato held that each such individuation was, *modo et forma*, an imperfect material copy of an Ideal Form, in much the same way that a fragment of a hologram is a more or less unresolved and reduced facsimile of the whole plate, which, in turn, is a perfect image of the object it reflects, in all of its dimensions.

As suggested in previous chapters, morphogenetic change in a species is initiated by a collective shift in special consciousness. This principle is the implicit theme in Plato's theory. For each Ideal Form is an Idea that reflects an eternal attribute of Universal Mind. These are the highest facets of mind's essence, culminating in the qualities of Truth, Beauty, and Good.

We concur with Plato. Existence and life manifest in the terrestrial limitations of time, space, and form but aspire upward through purposeful, developmental stages of progressively increasing consciousness, to a state of greater unity and fulfillment that transcends physical existence (space, time, and form)—the pure being of mind. The evolutionary cycles of life, death, transformation are the processes to achieving this ultimate state, both psychic and physical, with the former holding dynamic primacy.

Rupert Sheldrake states that there is a "vast gulf" between form, which is a qualitative aspect of everyday, direct experience, and "the quantitative factors with which physics concerns itself: mass momentum, energy, temperature, pressure, electric charge, etc." He notes further (in discussing such things as plants, butterflies, and bones), "As forms they are simply themselves; they cannot be reduced to anything else." For Sheldrake, morphogenetic fields are the invisible templates of form, of which gravitation, electromagnetism, and other energy fields are but discoverable components.

These are the experimental frontiers of science that are opening up new vistas of understanding of the relationship between mind, matter, metaphysics, and, in evolution, metamorphosis of form. It may well be that today's ablest and boldest scientists and evolutionists are reaching into territories of truth traversed by Plato and other thinkers millennia ago. Now falls to us in the modern age the task of further exploring and developing the higher ground of the mind, the manifesting destiny of humankind.

Chapter Seventeen

THE LARGER PICTURE

Just as the only species—man—that could dominate practically all the others on the planet had to be many times as intelligent as they, so the only hope for human government will be a level of intelligent life more mature still. The ancient annals, as we have seen, endorse and confirm this conclusion, and furnish the additional information that at previous critical junctures in human history, stages of evolution so far beyond man that he called them "gods" did indeed beneficiently intervene. The global crisis of the late 20th century shows all the signs of some extraordinary history repeating itself.

Kenneth Demarest,
The Winged Power

As much as some of its practitioners might like to believe, science cannot be partitioned off from other areas of life. Like religion, art, education, politics, culture, and society, it is an interdependent form of activity and inquiry, with the human being as both its progenitor and beneficiary. As Vico indicated, culture shapes thinking and theory, and theory can in turn reshape culture. Undoubtedly the potent disseminations of such thinkers as Plato, Aristotle, Copernicus, Descartes, Newton, Marx, Einstein, and Freud had a profound effect upon the course of civilization. They are prime examples of ideas and theories that more or less readily found a favorable *Zeitgeist* or mental climate for their propagation.

The Englishman Herbert Spencer (1820–1903) was one of the most highly regarded philosophers of his day and one of the most influential. Alfred Russel Wallace considered him "the greatest all-round thinker and most illuminating reasoner of the Nineteenth Century." Darwin himself deferred to Spencer as "about a dozen times my superior" and "by far the greatest living philosopher in England; perhaps equal to any who have lived."

Spencer formulated a theory of evolution known as The Developmental Hypothesis or the "universal theory" of evolution. By universal he meant that everything in the cosmos—stars, planets, life forms, mind, and even society—were receptive to evolutionary forces. According to this concept everything was thus either in a state of evolution, stasis, or dissolution. Spencer coined that fateful (and perhaps fatal) term "survival of the fittest" nine years before *Origin of Species* was published, and, although later embracing Darwin's idea of natural selection, he considered Lamarck's principle of the inheritance of acquired characteristics to be the more fundamental dynamic in evolution (especially human evolution).

Due to the powerful influence of scientific materialism and the technologically oriented social system that developed in the West, Darwin's concept of natural selection took root rapidly and deeply, like a mutant vegetation that chokes out other species. Spencer's followers generally ignored his Lamarckian leanings and seized upon his selectionist idea as a catch-all principle for most evolutionary phenomena. Spencer's 1850 book *Social Statistics* was considered the definitive work, from which they selectively lifted the "survival of the fittest" metonymy and helped sew the seeds of what is today called social Darwinism. Business and industrial tycoons like Rockefeller and Carnegie were highly affected by Spencer's writings and interpreted them to justify their actions and beliefs. And just as business tycoons utilized Darwin's and Spencer's "survival of the fittest" doctrine to justify laissez-faire capitalism, Karl Marx looked to Darwinism as a means to rationalize socialism. Writing in 1860, Marx stated that "Darwin's book

[*Origin of Species*] is very important and serves me as a basis in natural science for the class struggle in history." Socialists, then, saw entrepreneurship as a lower, animalistic form of endeavor, which, in Thorstein Veblen's words (*The Theory of the Leisure Class*) was the sign of "predatory aptitudes and propensities carried over by heredity and tradition from the barbarian past of the race." Marx's political philosophy of dialectical and historical materialism blended well with Darwinian scientific-mechanistic materialism. Such materialism could easily do away with mind, design, and higher intelligence. In socialistic-communistic political philosophy, history is the story of the distribution of material goods, and such history is determined by the action of human beings, not fate or supernatural forces ("Men make history, not the other way around").

But, as we stretch science to its limits and beyond, we are beginning to realize that materialism, mechanistics, and accident do not and cannot account for the facts as we now know them. In physics, where science has now reached its most advanced levels and where theory has moved beyond the law of pure mechanics, the stuff of life is being revealed more and more to resemble the properties of consciousness. We are reminded again of Sir James Jeans' reflection, "The universe begins to look more like a great thought than a great machine." And, "Mind no longer appears as an accidental intruder into the realm of matter; we are beginning to suspect that we ought rather to hail it as the creator and governor of the realm of matter."

It is absurd to regard mind, as the Darwinians do, as incidental. Rather, it not only appears to be causal but may be responsible for design, matter, and the coding of matter. The further we delve into it, mind and its coordinate, intelligence, seem to linger manifestly behind (or within) matter, evolution, and all of life.

Now that scientific man is beginning to pass beyond pure materialism, it is likely that this revered sentiment will diffuse into all of society as well. If so, this would bring us full circle to the foundations of ancient wisdom, which has always held that mind and intelligence pervade the universe and that design and purpose lie behind life and evolution.

A. E. Wilder Smith, in his book *The Creation of Life*, has examined and explicated many of the same points made above, and he has arrived at the conclusion that "the facts of design and designer are self-evident." He notes that this position corresponds with all our practical experience of life (actually, an "open-minded" experience of life) and, hence, must be considered an axiom of life. Using the analogy of our mind as a coffee mill, he points out that foolish thoughts are like stones and that feeding our thinking processes ("thought mill") with stones ("indigestible thought objects, like maintaining that codes and order arose spontaneously out of randomness") will damage the mind. By that, he means that these stones can literally damage our ability to "think straight." Smith proceeds into theology, quoting Romans 1:20–22: "Although they knew God, they did not honor him as God or give thanks to him, but they became futile in their thinking and their senseless minds were darkened. Claiming to be wise, they became fools." Smith then adjures us to (1) recognize the designer-design relationship, and (2) honor and serve the designer.

Although it is not our purpose to impose religion upon our readers, we would agree that while Darwinism has been essentially successful in convincing us of the reality of evolution, it has failed miserably (i.e., it has had certain destructive consequences) due to its ill-founded explanation of the process. A new or different evolutionary world view would not only fit the facts of life and development better, but would abet a *Zeitgeist* (already in our midst) that attempts to elevate humanity above its present dismal level, obsessed as it is with meaninglessness and mass annihilation.

In their recent book *The Dehumanization of Man*, Ashley Montagu and Floyd Matson dissect and examine modern society, noting its "culture of nihilism" and "disease of the spirit," much of it rooted in a "self-destructive science." Although not pointing the finger directly at Darwinism, the authors sense the origins of humanity's dehumanization as rooted in "imperatives of the modern world—money, mechanism, and materialism."

Though Darwin himself believed in God, nonetheless his theory was fundamentally nontheistic. In attempting to account for the evolution of *Homo sapiens* and the emergence of humankind's distinctive, higher qualities, he doggedly stuck to his basic explanatory principle, natural selection.

Alfred Russel Wallace—the cofounder, with Darwin, of the theory of natural selection—was by training and temperament a skeptical man. Most of his Victorian English peers considered him a natural scientist every bit the equal of Charles Darwin. Wallace's "survival of the fittest" vision came simultaneously with Darwin's, but quite independently and in a most cognitively different way. Wallace's was a classic bolt from the blue while gripped in a fever on a field trip in the Molucca Islands (today's eastern Indonesia) in February 1858. Literally "feverishly," he put it to paper that same night and mailed it to Darwin on the next ship to England. Upon receiving it, the latter's usual composure must have shifted to incredulity. For Darwin had just completed his own treatise, *Origin of Species*, on the very same concept! But unlike Wallace's inspiration, his was a long-labored idea that developed over several decades.

During the latter half of his life Wallace was a self-professed and unabashed spiritualist. His firsthand experience of nonordinary effects such as telepathy, seance phenomena, and automatic writing convinced him that there were various unknown (i.e., psychophysical) influences operating upon and through the human species and that natural selection, as he and Darwin had described it at least, was an inadequate explanation of the evolutionary process. Of these influences he wrote, in *On Modern Miracles and Spiritualism*: "They compelled me to accept them as facts, long before I could accept the spiritual explanation of them: there was at that time no place in my fabric of thought into which it could be fitted. By slow degrees a place was made."

A "fabric of thought" is a curious entity. Depending upon the individual or the society, it can be expanded, elaborated, created anew, or rigidified and eventually warped. Obviously, certain events had taken place in Wallace's life to keep his "fabric of thought" both expansive and flexible. Whether or not we wish to take his testimony to the occult at face value, it should be noted here that he lost no stature in the scientific community of his day for his interest in it. On the contrary, he became an esteemed member of learned societies (he was president of the Entomological Society of London, 1870 to 1887) and continued to publish numerous authoritative books, articles, and tracts. In 1890 he was awarded the first Darwin medal of the Royal Society. He remained a robust thinker all of his life, always a questioner. He rarely leaped to extra-natural reasons for inexplicable phenomena. Of his and Darwin's mutual convergence on the notion of natural selection, he might well have gone no further than Darwin's own observation: "I never saw a more striking coincidence."

It has often been said that a coincidence is simply an event with unknown connections to other events or things. Could it have been that there was some thread of a "thought fabric" between Darwin in England and Wallace a half a world away in the Moluccas? If so, was it the thread with which Wallace began unconsciously weaving new patterns into his thinking about organic processes and human development? We have no way of knowing, at least logically.

A *Zeitgeist* is a psychic ambiance enveloping an entire epoch, a whole civilization. Everything cultural takes place within it. But like any mood or atmosphere, it is transitory and phase-subjective. Its phases are contractive or expansive, varying in propensities of wisdom, knowledge, creativity, and life-affirmation or in ignorance and life-diminishment. When the latter manifests in abundance, as history has shown, the *Zeitgeist* itself breaks down rapidly, bringing down a civilization with it. More commonly, however, the phase-shift is gradual and inexorable. The *Zeitgeist* is today surely changing, for reasons that hopefully have been glimpsed by the reader in the preceding pages.

The need for a broad, new evolutionary world view or paradigm has been stressed throughout this book. A critical-mass principle seems to operate in shifting a world view: when enough individuals or segments of society share them (after perceiving the need), the world view changes via a general heightening of collective consciousness. There are indications now that a truly global consciousness is engirdling planet earth, and one far more manifest than some wishful "Age of Aquarius." The sociopolitical, economic, religious, scientific, and metaphysical spheres are all undergoing major, and in some instances rapid, change. As a complex, these spheres form a kind of psychomental network that the eminent Jesuit theosopher Teilhard de Chardin called the "noosphere."*

It is now passé to say that such prophets as Teilhard were far ahead of their time. However, the fact needs reiteration that they themselves were exemplifications of the evolving human consciousness they heralded. Their legacies have weathered the materialistic *Zeitgeist* and are daily being strengthened by the rigors of a new, open-minded science. Teilhard's noosphere, for example, is definitively identical to Rupert Sheldrake's "field of causative formation." The two models are connected by the very dynamic of global mind they describe. It is a dynamic that transcends both time and space, and conceivably any culture-bound *Zeitgeist*. Jung's theory of the racial archetype and the collective unconscious is a similar framework for a mind-at-large reality.

Darwin's (and Wallace's) theory of evolution by natural selection became deeply entrenched in Western thought because it meshed so completely with the materialistic *Zeitgeist* of its day. It conceptually buttressed other reductionistic formulations of the century such as logical positivism in philosophy and, later, behaviorism in psychology. All emphasized the visible, measurable, and controllable against what was not. Thus they gave the body primacy over the mind. Since Descartes had two centuries earlier separated them as functional entities, it was easy for Darwin and others to view the body as disassociated from the mind. Because it was so solidly accessible to sensible measurement, it was considered the only half of the dualism that was objectively "real" and worthy of study. Within this paradigm it was logical for Darwin to see organisms as animated objects. The fittest anatomies survived, and evolved.

This reductionistic construct has maintained a stranglehold on evolutionary thought up to the present day. But there are sure signs that

---

*Annotation, "The Evolution of Evolution."

its grip is being broken. Numerous, unprecedented indictments of Darwinian premises, based on the latest research, are coming from respected scientists in various disciplines. Mind and consciousness have been readmitted into science as valid subjects for study, and in some areas (e.g., self-development, paranormal studies) they occupy center stage. A world view is emerging that sees the universe and everything in it as alive and evolving. The earth itself is beginning to be perceived in the new global consciousness as the autonomous and intricately beautiful organism it is, a Web of Life still being woven. All of these developments are flourishing proof that higher consciousness is no other-worldly myth. The Darwinian edifice is creaking in the strong winds of change.

Transformism is a one-word description of all the above. As an alternative theory of evolution it may never be as timely as now. It is a worldview sorely needed in the uncertainties and anxieties of our shifting *Zeitgeist*. It can aid us in directing and stabilizing our rate of change, to alter its course when and where necessary. Most importantly it allows—no, requires—a personal hand from each of us in these processes.

Evolution is transformation. It is happening now, often in the baffling events and experiences unique and common to each of us. That wonder is all too easily obscured by specialist preoccupations with fossil records, genetic theory, and so forth. Thus we might tend to think of evolution, if at all, as something occurring in the past or future, with present life forms (including ourselves) suspended in a kind of developmental limbo pending the next new patent of mutational change. As the Darwinists would have it, all we can do is wait.

Nothing is further from the facts. For millennia the wisest of people have pronounced that nothing remains the same and that destiny demands cooperation for its fulfillment. Those who remain strangers to that truth fall back on chance, coincidence, and a helpless fate.

ANNOTATIONS

MICROCOMPUTERS AND MEMORY

As an information storage system, the brain/gene has an interesting analogy in the modern computer. Recently there has been much ado about computer or "silicon" evolution. This concept carries elements of truth, though it takes on aspects of the bizarre when projected as independent of human evolution. The differences between the two may be as instructive as the similarities.

Artificial Intelligence (AI) is devoted to computer simulation of human behavior and intelligence, that is, the human brain. It is well known that microcomputers and robots (*hardware*) have now been created that can play a respectable game of chess, carry on a rudimentary conversation, solve and traverse mazes, walk the dog, fetch the newspaper, entertain guests, and more. To perform these marvels the computer must have, as the brain does, a program (*software*) comprised of bits ("bytes" in AI argot) of information, one for each task. The three basic kinds of programs are called "memory," and they roughly correspond to the three levels of memory in our organismic model:

HUMAN	AI
Short-term—Rudimentary attention span. Conscious, active, temporary. Material disappears in 10–20 seconds if not repeated; remembering numbers, location of objects, etc. Limited storage capacity (approx. seven items at a time).	*Random access* (RAM)—Allows replacement of old information with new at very rapid speed. Analogous to continually changing information an organism must respond to in its environment. Large storage capacity. Forms: memory chips and "cards" (plastic slabs of extensive chip combinations and/or integrated circuitry).
Medium-range—Learned experiences. Higher cerebral functions requiring repetition, sustained feedback. Emotive and cognitive.	*External*—Archival, memory of record. Consists of "software" and processed information resulting from software application; semi-permanent. Stored on disks and cassette.
Racial—Pangenerational, genetic transfer of developing, general characteristics; behavior and morphogenesis. The transmutational brain/genome system.	*Read-only* (ROM)—Fixed, wired-in, automatic programs. Operational even when power is cut. Permanent (as compared to RAM), "silicon" subconsciousness.

The immense, and conceivably infinite, quantitative and qualitative differences between human and computer memory make a one-to-one correspondence invalid and misleading. Unlike the human, silicon memory is completely mechanistic, programmatically sequential, and devoid of the holistic cognitive modes of feeling and intuition. Human experiences are carbon-, not silicon-based. However, assuming the general analogy between AI and human memory to be valid, it becomes more clear why the Darwinian evolutionary model is inadequate. For no happy accident or "mutation," regardless of the odds, will improve a computer memory chip. Any programmer will laugh at the absurdity of the idea. Is it any different for the human gene, a vastly more complex system? Consider, then, the even greater absurdity implied when any margin of error or accident is allowed in memory coding from short-term and medium-term memory in the brain to "access" the genome.

Although critics may raise objections to any comparison between human evolution and development of AI, it can be countered that the more recently created "biochip" bridges the metaphorical gap. This is the "organic computer," which is almost *identical* to its human counterpart and, like it, requires no external source of electricity, as well as being self-assembling.

BIOENGINEERING AND EVOLUTION

The technological advancements achieved in genetic engineering are nothing short of amazing, and they herald much for the betterment of humankind and the modern world. To date, techniques of gene manipulation (splicing, etc.) have been successful in getting bacteria to synthesize human proteins like insulin and interferon, and botanists are now experimenting with similar procedures, such as artificially recombining DNA, in plant production. The possibilities in this field seem almost unlimited, including producing bacteria capable of manufacturing vitamins, antibiotics (and other antibodies), fertilizers, dyes, and much more.

Since genetic engineering entails direct control over the action of genes, it is not surprising that many biologists are becoming interested in its capacity to alter the course of organismic evolution. Hence, in their book entitled *The Laws of Chance*, authors Manfred Eigen and Ruthild Winkler suggest that "it is quite conceivable that by combining genetic materials from different sources, experiments in evolution may produce new kinds of beings," And in a recent *Omni* (November 1983) article entitled "Soul Genetics," Yvonne Baskin suggests that genetic manipulation could be used to change human nature, intelligence, behavior, and ultimately human evolution for the better.

Though some, like Jeremy Rifkin, fear the accidental escape of a manmade "doomsday bug," there seems to be no convincing argument against prudent research in this vast and potentially fruitful area. We do caution, however, against headlong applications of this technology, which favor short-term gains, while long-term effects are still questionable or pose high-stake risks. Gene-tampering may indeed be the answer to increase crop yields to feed the world's hungry, to provide viable energy supplements, to synthesize drugs, and more. In some cases, however, the advantages have not been adequately weighed against risks, or they have been simply glossed over by eager technocrats.

As for "producing new kinds of beings," it can first be pointed out that Mother Nature has been busy at this very task since the first seed of life floated in the oceanic womb of earth eons ago. She is the prolific and unsurpassed handmaiden of evolution on this planet. In contrast, bioengineers do not actually create new forms but simply juggle the mechanics of old ones, thereby altering the functions and secondary morphogenetic characteristics (increasing or decreasing size, hybridizing shapes). As discussed throughout this book, primary life forms are coefficients of consciousness. We can "make" a new strain (hybrid) of species, but we cannot make a new species from scratch. Thus, biogeneticists will not create "new beings," but rather impressive variations on extant ones.

Bioengineers, scientific animal breeders, and neo-Darwinists share a common outlook; their visions of formal and functional improvement seldom take into account a species' possible development outside of a materialistic and mechanistic exploitation. Consequently, between "survival of the fittest" logic and high-yield concerns, most of the thinking leaves little room for a theory of development that goes beyond the reductive shortfalls of both.

Evolution is a multidimensional, directive process that is finally unamenable to efforts of uncontexted manipulation. Still we may be able to cooperate with and enhance nature's designs for the general good of all, benefiting at the same time from human-engineered, unlethal variations of living forms. At present we had best look upon genetic engineering as but a sophisticated, technically impressive tinkering that, like many another technology, can be used for good or ill.

Perfection is already inherent in natural evolution. We have barely an inkling of its techniques of perfection, and the uncovering of these will perhaps make bioengineering look like a game of Scrabble indeed. Sheldrake's "principle of causative formation," Bergson's "life force," and perhaps even telepathy are windows opened on the larger mystery of life and evolution. If we can understand these phenomena, we will come closer to engineering our own greater perfection of harmony with nature's other beings, both genetically and nongenetically.

THE EVOLUTION OF EVOLUTION

Thus we men, as God transmutes himself into one, we likewise on earth should resign ourselves and become one.
                                                                  Paracelsus

Time has always been one of the central mysteries of people's experience, though at the personal level their most unconsciously familiar. Many people's thoughts about time seldom get free of the image of the tedious sweep of a clock's hands, the diminishing days and months of a calendar, or perhaps the connected memories of ineffaceable dates: anniversaries, births, deaths. A wrinkle here or a gray hair there may prompt some individuals to deeper contemplation of their "allotted time" on earth, but for most temporality is singularly personal, rarely considered in a suprapersonal or transpersonal context.

As modern physics has well established, however, time is relative and subjective. This is most true on the human level, and we can say that any facet of higher knowledge, such as evolution, must be grasped with a more objective sense of time. This comes of meditating on processes of a larger timescale than one's own. The historical timescale is a good place to begin in approaching evolutionary timescale. Those who have a "feel" for march of historical events and dialectics may begin to expand that sense to the rather visionary one of evolutionary reality, and it could well be that he who truly apprehends the latter has also intuited the essence of time.

For our purpose here, let us assume that time is simply the movement of consciousness in evolution. Try to imagine this movement in the mineral realm, time almost frozen but not quite. Next the primitive plant and animal world, time thawing out a little more as consciousness picks up a slight bit of speed. With fish and reptiles we begin to get a slow but inexorable trickle of time and consciousness. The more lively amphibians increase the pace a little, and with the appearance of mammals and feathered birds things are definitely flowing. Finally comes man with a veritable torrent of consciousness, his thought velocity quickening apace up to the present movement.

The swift current of human consciousness and intelligence has carried people to the awareness of evolution, and now their minds strain yet more to comprehend its ultimate purpose. With this phenomenon a great mental milestone has been reached, one that we will call the "evolution of evolution." Mind has begun to reflect on mind, to probe the function and meaning of its own evolution. The *accelerating rate of conscious evolution* has brought humanity to this point.

People have conceived of a hierarchy of consciousness, intelligence, and being: the idea that the universe itself is in evolution—but for what purpose? If there is a creator of this universe, why would he set it in evolutionary motion? Why create this unfathomable dynamic called "consciousness" with all its ecstasies, trials, and tortures? Might God himself evolve? Is this where what we call "thought" itself must stop?

No definitive answers to these questions can be given here. Nonetheless, there are teleological models in ancient and modern philosophies, set forth by the wisest of humankind, which tend to converge on common themes and explanations, and which can answer the questions for those who can absorb meaning beyond words. The following is a condensed diagrammatic framework for such a cosmology:[1]

> If we look for the nearest place to us in the universe we realize that we live on the earth, and that the moon is under the influence of the earth. At the same time we see that the earth is one of the planets of the solar system, that there are bigger planets, probably more powerful than the earth, and that all these planets, taken together, must somehow affect and control the earth. Next in scale comes the sun, and we realize that the sun controls all the planets and the earth at the same time. If you think from this point of view you will already have a different idea of the solar system, although there is nothing new in these things: it is only a question of how to relate one thing to another.

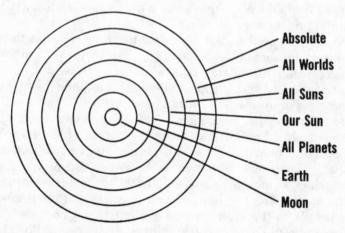

Absolute

All Worlds

All Suns

Our Sun

All Planets

Earth

Moon

[1]P. D. Ouspensky, *The Fourth Way* (New York: Vintage/Random House, 1971 [1957]), pp. 23–24.

Earth is one of the planets of the solar system and the sun is one of the stars of the Milky Way. Beyond that we can take all possible worlds. This is all we know from the ordinary point of view. As a purely philosophical term we can add to that a condition or relationship of things which we call the Absolute, a state in which everything is one. Now we can express this relation of moon to earth, earth to planets, and so on in a slightly different way.

- Absolute. Unknown beginning of all.
- All Worlds. All galaxies similar and dissimilar to our galaxy.
- All Suns. Our galaxy.
- Our Sun. Our solar system.
- All Planets. All planets of the solar system.
- Earth.
- Moon.

If we take the Absolute as "Creator" in this scheme, we may conceive that he issues the universe(s) into existence out of the total unity of his pure being. Our cosmos and others may be but a single facet or possibility out of the infinite spectrum of his attributes, each with its own hierarchical degrees of consciousness. Each level is qualitatively superior to that below it and possibly has powers of guidance or impulsion over it, just as we observe the general principle on earth (humans over monkeys, etc.).

Supposing that terrestrial humans are susceptible to the influence of superior forms of intelligence, of which they are generally unaware, what would possibly be the purpose of such influence? One school of thought is that it is in the service of evolutionary design. In the hierarchy, each level of being/consciousness is a servitor of and answerable to that above it. Yet there is no compulsion, at least on the planes beyond the human, only mutual attraction. Thus evolution becomes more spiritual and less material as consciousness ascends from a lower gradation to a higher. And even as humans are beyond monkeys, there are people beyond people. These visible individuals would be the agents of invisible beings. Arcane as this relationship might seem, it would be a quite logical and natural one in the greater design.

At the grossest material levels of our universe reside, we may assume, the lowest forms of consciousness, those which are most fragmented and unreflective of the original issuance of the Creator. But this level is no less purposeful in the design than higher ones; indeed for humankind the material world may be a severe workshop essential to the forging and refining of the spirit. Here, even "good" and "evil" are relative. The former is whatever accelerates evolutionary consciousness, the latter whatever decelerates it.

And what return does the Creator get out of all of this? Any answer in prose is apt to sound sacrilegiously crude, so the reader is invited to weigh this thought against whatever he or she may feel within about a Creator and his creation: He creates because he wishes to reflect back into himself his infinite attributes, as in a mirror (cosmoses), from the void of nonexistence into the manifest light of his Pure Being. And he creates because it is one of his possibilities.

THE FUTURE HUMAN

Because Darwinism relies mainly upon the caprice of chance mutation for explaining evolution, it is not so surprising that it is essentially at a loss in presenting credible predictions of future human development. What prognostications are made by Darwinists are so outlandishly removed (hybrid man-animal-machines) from the present human form as to be irrelevant.

On the other hand, many non-Darwinist theorists see considerable value in examining the possibilities of the future human. If, in fact, we today are setting courses for the future, it is most important to know the directions in which human development is headed and if any of the courses might be altered.

In keeping with the theme of this book, we ascribe to the brain the function of evolutionary guidance, and believe therefore that study of it can tell us the most regarding future man. As a start, consider the accompanying graph, which charts the change in human brain size over the past 10 million years.

A pattern is certainly apparent here. The gradual enlargement of the brain (in proportion to body weight) over epochs rules out any randomly inclined influence and establishes a definite continuity of growth. Barring a man-made or natural global catastrophe, the future evolution of the human brain appears assured.

Extrapolating from the graph, the "chances" for a larger human brain 10 million years from now seem probable indeed. An increase in brainpower (or mindpower) must inevitably accompany this physical growth of the organ. Naturally, a larger brain will require a larger skull and head, and we can also reasonably assume that the trend of overall decrease in body mass in proportion to these will also continue. Thus, with more intelligence future man will surely develop advanced forms of automation (robotics), which will, in turn, diminish the need for sheer bodily strength and mass. Perhaps further development of the

EVOLUTION OF THE HUMAN BRAIN

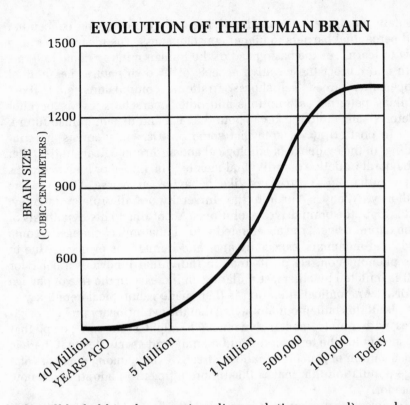

body will be held in abeyance (pending evolutionary need) or undergo subtle anatomical refinements.

However, our graph (based upon comparative skull size) also shows us that human brain enlargement has generally leveled off for about the last 100,000 years. We believe, nonetheless, that mental evolution has not likewise abated during this period and that the internal organization of the brain has continued to evolve, or has at least rearranged its infrastructure in correspondence with the increasing sophistication of human intelligence. In this light, man's future brain evolution might best be understood in terms of an ongoing fluctuation and reorganization of the inner structures of the cerebrum.

Another major and related consideration is the fact that the human cortex has developed at a rate vastly unprecedented in evolutionary history. The growth plateau previously mentioned might be explainable in the context of unexploited potential. Does a species ever acquire a larger brain if the resources of its present one are not tapped in *toto*? We think the answer is no.

The future evolution of the human brain, then, is best foreseen in the framework of the human mind. Since its full potential mindpower is already there, humankind's evolutionary possibilities must be fundamentally contingent upon identifying and removing the conceptual and perceptual barriers to higher consciousness. The idea of "learning how to learn," or the basic need of the human mind to come to terms with and correct the negative aspects of its own nature (*i.e.,* animal propensities; greed, selfishness, irrational compulsions, etc.), fixed thinking patterns, assumptions and other characteristics of "psychosclerosis" may hold the key to both the near and distant human future.

In postscript, we note that some pro-Darwin theorists are conceding (in the evidence of ethological and anthropological studies) that behavioral initiative of individual members of animal or human groups often anticipates or triggers like behavior en masse. One leading authority, Allan C. Wilson of the University of California at Berkeley, states that "the brain drives evolution." According to his hypothesis of "behavioral drive," the accelerated rate of anatomical change in some birds and mammals, especially apes and humans, is primarily due to this phenomenon. He posits that an individual innovates a behavior that is imitated by others, stimulating an increase in the rate of change of DNA. Anatomical alteration is then made genotypical/hereditary.

Is all this tantamount to saying that the evolutionary process originates with purely mental dynamics? It might seem so—except that Wilson avoids the terms *mind* and *mental*, and speculates that there is a distribution of genetic mutations already extant among members of a large population that makes them more efficient in adopting the new behavior.

"Selective pressures" produced by the brain, "behavioral drives" and like phrases are technical euphemisms for processes that are fundamentally nonphysical (mental) in nature. Postulating some preexistent, random genetic mutation favorable to these processes seems an almost sophistic way of attempting to maintain the Darwinist necessity for the primacy of a random, physical factor in evolution.

If there are indeed genes already disposed to the accommodation of a novel behavior, the definitive question then must be, did it get that way by random mutation—or by intention?

NOTES

Preface

1. Edward de Bono, *The Use of Lateral Thinking* (London: Jonathan Cape, 1967), p. 26.

2. Henryk Skolimowski, *Eco-Philosophy* (Boston: Marion Boyars, 1981), p. 107.

3. Erwin Schroedinger, *ibid.*, pp. 70–71.

One

1. Theodosius Dobzhansky, *et al.*, *Evolution* (San Francisco: W. H. Freeman, 1975), p. 8.

2. Guy Murchie, *The Seven Mysteries of Life* (Boston: Houghton Mifflin Co., 1981), p. 541.

3. *Ibid.*, p. 542.

Two

1. Lewis Thomas, "On the Nature of Cooperation." *Discover* (November 1981), p. 59.

2. Arthur Koestler, *Janus* (New York: Random House, 1978), pp. 159–160.

3. John C. Greene, *Science, Ideology, and the World View* (Berkeley: University of California Press, 1981), p. 8.

4. Leon Pompa, "Vico's Theory of the Causes of Historical Change." *Institute for Cultural Research Monographs* (London: Octagon Press, 1971), p. 12.

Three

1. Shirley Sugerman, ed., *Evolution of Consciousness* (Middletown, Conn.: Wesleyan University Press, 1976), p. 69.

2. Henryk Skolimowski, "Evolutionary Illuminations." *Alternative Futures* (Fall 1980), p. 10.

3. *Ibid.*, p. 10.

Four

1. Henryk Skolimowski, "Evolutionary Illuminations." *Alternative Futures* (Fall 1980), pp. 7–8.

2. Itzhak Bentov, *Stalking the Wild Pendulum* (New York: E.P. Dutton, 1977), p. 95.

3. *Ibid.*, p. 96.

4. *Ibid.*

5. Malcom Ross MacDonald, *The Origin of Johnny* (New York: Knopf, 1975), p. 8.

6. *Ibid.*, p. 13.

Five

1. Josh McDowell and Don Stewart, *Answers to Tough Questions* (San Bernardino: Here's Life Publishers, 1980), p. 89.

2. Desmond Morris, *The Naked Ape* (New York: Dell, 1967), p. 19.

Six

1. Jalalludin Rumi, *The Masnavi: Teachings of Rumi* (London: Octagon Press, 1973), pp. 216–217.

2. Theodore Roszak, *Unfinished Animal* (New York: Harper and Row, 1975), p. 99.

3. *Ibid.*, p. 99.

4. Charles Darwin, *The Origin of Species* (New York: Mentor, 1958), p. 88.

5. *Ibid.*, p. 34.

6. Arthur Koestler, *Janus* (New York: Random House, 1978), pp. 196–197.

7. Edward O. Wilson, *Sociobiology* (Cambridge: Belknap Press, 1980).

8. David P. Barash, *Sociobiology and Behavior* (New York: Elsevier, 1977).

9. Motoo Kimura, "The Neutral Theory of Molecular Evolution." *Scientific American* (November 1979).

10. Edward O. Wilson, *Sociobiology*, pp. 32–49.

11. *Ibid.*, p. 3.

12. Richard Dawkins, *The Selfish Gene* (New York: Oxford University Press, 1976), p. iv.

13. Stephen J. Gould, "Is a New and General Theory of Evolution Emerging?" *Paleobiology* 6, no. 1, 1980.

14. *Ibid.*, p. 121.

15. Eric Jantsch, *The Self-Organizing Universe* (New York: Pergamon Press, 1980), p. 224.

Seven

1. Robert Nisbet, *Prejudices* (Cambridge: Harvard University Press, 1982), p. 79.
2. Mark Davidson, *Uncommon Sense* (Los Angeles: Tarcher, 1983), p. 98.
3. Colin Wilson, *The Occult* (New York: Vintage/Random House, 1973), p. 141.
4. Ashleigh Brilliant, *I May Not Be Totally Perfect* (Santa Barbara: Woodbridge, 1972), p. 115.
5. Theodore Roszak, *Unfinished Animal* (New York: Harper and Row, 1975), p. 102.
6. M. Kasha and B. Pullmin, eds., *Horizons in Biochemistry* (London: Academic Press, 1962), p. 174.
7. W. H. Thorpe, *Animal Nature and Human Nature* (New York: Anchor/Doubleday, 1974), p. 35.
8. F. B. Salisbury, "Natural Selection and the Complexity of the Gene." *Nature* 224 (1969), pp. 342–343.
9. John C. Fiddes, "The Nucleotide Sequence of a Viral DNA." *Scientific American* (December 1977), pp. 64–65.
10. Paul S. Moorhead and Martin S. Kaplan, eds., *Mathematical Challenges to the Neo-Darwinian Interpretation of Evolution* (Philadelphia: Wistar Institute Press), pp. 73–80.
11. Mark Davidson, *Uncommon Sense*, pp. 90–91.
12. A. E. Wilder-Smith, *The Creation of Life* (Wheaton, Ill.: H. Shaw, 1970), pp. 26–27.
13. Theodore Roszak, *Unfinished Animal*, p. 102.
14. Cecil P. Martin, *Psychology, Evolution, and Sex* (Springfield: Charles C. Thomas, Publisher, 1956), pp. 77–83.
15. Theodosius Dobzhansky, *et al.*, *Evolution* (San Francisco: W. H. Freeman, 1975), p. 65.
16. *Ibid.*, p. 66.
17. *Ibid.*, p. 72.
18. Arthur Koestler, *Janus* (New York: Random House, 1978), pp. 186–188.
19. C. P. Martin, *Psychology, Evolution, and Sex*, p. 65.
20. J. R. Smythies and Arthur Koestler, eds., *Beyond Reductionism* (London: Hutchinson, 1969), pp. 65–66.
21. C. P. Martin, *Psychology, Evolution, and Sex*, p. 79.

22. Carl C. Lindegren, *Cold War in Biology* (Ann Arbor: Planarian Press, 1966), p. 75.

23. John A. Wiens, "Competition or Peaceful Coexistence?" *Natural History* (March 1983), p. 30.

24. *Ibid.*, p. 34.

25. J. R. Smythies and Arthur Koestler, eds., *Beyond Reductionism*, pp. 67–68.

26. Carl C. Lindegren, *Cold War in Biology*, p. 67.

27. Fred Hoyle, *The Intelligent Universe* (New York: Holt, Rinehart and Winston, 1984), p. 123.

28. J. R. Smythies and Arthur Koestler, eds., *Beyond Reductionism*, p. 81.

29. C. S. Sherrington, *ibid.*, pp. 44–45.

30. Lawrence E. Gilbert and Peter H. Raven, eds., *Coevolution of Animals and Plants* (Austin: University of Texas Press, 1975), p. 210.

31. Eric R. Planka, *Evolutionary Ecology* (New York: Harper and Row, 1978), p. 166.

32. Rachel Wilder, "Made for Each Other." *Science Digest* (September 1981), p. 107.

33. Lewis Thomas, *ibid.*, p. 107.

34. Theodore Roszak, *Unfinished Animal*, p. 101.

35. Arthur M. Young, *The Reflexive Universe* (New York: Delacorte Press, 1976), pp. 174–175.

36. Owen Barfield, *Saving the Appearances* (New York: Harcourt Brace Jovanovich, 1976), p. 6.

Eight

1. R. Buckminster Fuller, *Operating Manual for Spaceship Earth* (New York: Pocket Books, 1970), p. 13.

2. Itzhak Bentov, *Stalking the Wild Pendulum* (New York: Dutton, 1977), pp. 114–115.

3. Mahmud Shabistari, *The Secret Garden*, trans. Johnson Pasha (London: Octagon Press, 1969), p. 26.

4. Joseph Chilton Pearce, *Magickal Child* (New York: Dutton, 1977), p. 6.

5. George Leonard, *The Silent Pulse* (New York: Bantam, 1981), pp. 69 and 79.

6. Arthur Koestler, *Janus* (New York: Random House, 1978), p. 25.

7. *Ibid.*, p. 16.

8. R. Buckminster Fuller, *Operating Manual for Spaceship Earth*, p. 64.

9. Arthur Koestler, *Janus*, p. 31.

10. William Wordsworth, "The Daisy," *Wordsworth: Poetry and Prose* (Cambridge: Harvard University Press, 1967), p. 563.

11. Gyorgy Doczi, *The Power of Limits* (Boulder: Shambhala, 1981), p. ix.

12. *Ibid.*, p. 1.

13. *Ibid.*, p. 5.

14. Guy Murchie, *The Seven Mysteries of Life* (Boston: Houghton Mifflin, 1978), p. 599.

Nine

1. Karl Victor, *Goethe* (Cambridge: Harvard University Press, 1950), p. 22.

2. *Ibid.*, p. 28.

3. *Ibid.*, p. 31.

4. *Ibid.*, p. 33.

5. H. Graham Cannon, *Lamarck and Modern Genetics* (Westport, Conn.: Greenwood Press, 1959), pp. 51–52.

6. Samuel Butler, *Unconscious Memory* (London: A. C. Fifield, 1910), p. 15.

7. Roland Gammon, "Scientific Mysticism." *New Realities* (December 1980), p. 11.

8. Samuel Butler, *Unconscious Memory*, pp. 5–6.

9. *Ibid.*, p. 68.

10. L. McDonald Schetby, "Shape-Memory Alloys." *Scientific American* (November 1979), p. 74.

11. Louis C. Kervran, *Biological Transmutations* (Binghamton, N.Y.: Swan House, 1972).

12. James L. Gould and Carol Grant Gould, "The Instinct to Learn." *Science 81* (May 1981), p. 45.

13. Fritjof Capra, *The Tao of Physics* (Boulder: Shambhala, 1975), p. 142.

14. Henri Bergson, *Creative Evolution* (New York: Random House, 1944), p. 84.

15. W. Tschernezky, "Dolphins and the Mind of Man." *New Scientist* (August 1968).

16. H. Bergson, *Creative Evolution*, pp. 74–75.

17. George Bernard Shaw, *Man and Superman* (Baltimore: Penguin, 1952), p. 152.

18. George Bernard Shaw, *Back to Methuselah* (New York: Oxford University Press, 1947), p. 76.

19. Friedrich Nietzsche, *Beyond Good and Evil* (New York: Vintage/Random House, 1966), pp. 213–214.

Ten

1. Theodore Roszak, *Unfinished Animal* (New York: Harper and Row, 1975), p. 104.

2. *Ibid.*, p. 105.

3. Charles Muses and Arthur Young, *Consciousness and Reality* (New York: Avon, 1972).

4. Jack L. King and Thomas H. Jukes, "Non-Darwinian Evolution." *Science*, May 16, 1969.

5. "Genes That Move to Fight Disease." *Newsweek*, September 22, 1980.

6. James F. Crow, "Genes That Violate Mendel's Rules." *Scientific American* (February 1979).

7. Stanley N. Cohen and James A. Shapiro, "Transposable Genetic Elements." *Scientific American* (February 1980).

8. "A New Type of Life." *Newsweek*, December 24, 1979.

9. Barry Commoner, "Role of Deoxyribonucleic Acid in Inheritance." *Nature*, June 6, 1964, p. 968.

10. Howard Temin, "RNA-Directed DNA Synthesis." *Scientific American* (January 1972).

11. Lester Smith, ed., *Intelligence Came First* (Wheaton, Ill.: Theosophical Publishing House, 1975), p. 126.

12. *Ibid.*, p. 126.

13. Carl Lindegren and Lynn Margulis, "Dogma and Iconoclasm in Biology: The Gene Is Not Enough." *Coevolution Quarterly* (Summer 1980), p. 68.

14. Ruth Sager, "Genes Outside the Chromosomes." *Scientific American* (January 1965), p. 79.

15. Bert W. O'Malley and William T. Schrader, "The Receptors of Steroid Hormones." *Scientific American* (February 1976).

16. Tom Marriates and Mark Ptashne, "A DNA-Repressor System." *Scientific American* (January 1976), p. 76.

17. Peter Beaconsfield, George Birdwood, and Rebecca Beaconsfield, "The Placenta." *Scientific American* (August 1950).

18. Bruce S. McEwen, "Interactions Between Hormones and Nerve Tissue." *Scientific American* (November 1972).

19. Julius Axelrod, "Neurotransmitters." *Scientific American* (June 1974).

20. Steven Rose, *The Conscious Brain* (New York: Vintage/Random House, 1976), p. 235.

21. J. R. Smythies and Arthur Koestler, eds., *Beyond Reductionism* (London: Hutchinson, 1968), p. 115.

22. *Ibid.*, pp. 96–97.

23. *Ibid.*, p 92.

24. E. Roy John, "Derepressor Hypothesis." *Mechanisms of Memory* (New York: Academic Press, 1967), p. 133.

25. R. B. Gorcynski and E. J. Steele, "Simultaneous Yet Independent Inheritance of Somatically Acquired Tolerance of Two Distinct U-2 Antigenic Haplotype Determinants in Mice." *Nature*, February 19, 1981, pp. 678–681.

26. Richard P. Novick, "Plasmids." *Scientific American* (February 1981), p. 110.

27. Manfred Eigen, *et al.*, "The Origin of Genetic Information." *Scientific American* (April 1981), p. 118.

28. James A. Nathanson and Paul Greengard, "Second Messengers in the Brain." *Scientific American* (August 1977), p. 108.

29. *Ibid.*, p. 119.

30. *Ibid.*

31. *Ibid.*

32. Eric R. Kandel, "Small Systems of Neurons." *Scientific American* (September 1979), p. 76.

33. Rae Silver and Harvey H. Feder, eds., *Hormones and Reproductive Behavior: Readings from Scientific American* (San Francisco: W. H. Freeman, 1979), p. 69.

34. David Crews, "The Hormonal Control of Behavior in a Lizard." *Scientific American* (August 1979).

35. *Ibid.*, pp. 185–186.

36. P. D. Ouspensky, *A New Model of the Universe* (New York: Vintage/Random House, 1971 [orig. 1931], pp. 453–454.

Eleven

1. Harold Saxton Burr, *The Fields of Life* (New York: Ballantine, 1972).

2. Joseph F. Goodavage, *Magic: Science of the Future* (New York: Signet, 1976), pp. 79–80.

3. David Epel, "The Problem of Fertilization." *Scientific American* (November 1977), p. 129.

4. Guy L. Playfair and Scott Hill, *The Cycles of Heaven* (New York: Avon, 1978), pp. 286–287.

5. Edward R. Russell, *Report on Radionics* (London: Neville Spearman, 1973).

6. D. G. Garan, *The Paradox of Pleasure and Relativity* (New York: Philosophical Library, 1963), pp. 434–435.

7. Rupert Sheldrake, *A New Science of Life* (London: Blond and Briggs, 1981).

8. Edward Campbell, "Some Unusual Aspects of Communication." *Institute for Cultural Research Monographs* (1977), pp. 7–9.

9. Rupert Sheldrake, "Hidden Force." *Science Digest* (October 1981), p. 56.

10. Raymond Van Over and Laura Oteri, eds., *William McDougall: Explorer of the Mind* (New York: Helix Press, 1967), p. 29.

11. *Ibid.*, p. 30.

12. Lewis Wolpert, "Pattern Formation in Biological Development." *Scientific American* (October 1978), pp. 155–156.

13. *Ibid.*, p. 164.

14. Bernard Dixon, "Shape Shapes Shape." *Omni* (October 1981), p. 20.

15. Sir Alister Hardy, *The Living Stream* (New York: Harper and Row, 1975), p. 257.

16. Lyle Watson, *Lifetide* (New York: Simon and Schuster, 1979), pp. 131–132.

Thirteen

1. Ernest Scott, *The People of the Secret* (London: Octagon, 1983), p. 251.

Fourteen

1. Lyle Watson, *Supernature* (New York: Bantam, 1973), p. 245.

2. John W. Saunders, Jr., *Patterns and Principles of Animal Development* (New York: Macmillan, 1970), p. 126.

3. Buckminster Fuller (with E. J. Applewhite), *Synergetics* (New York: Macmillan, 1975), p. 81.

4. *Ibid.*, pp. 82–83.

5. *Ibid.*, pp. 88–89.

6. Lawrence LeShan, *The Medium, the Mystic, and the Physicist* (New York: Ballantine, 1975).

7. Theodore Roszak, *Person/Planet* (New York: Anchor/Doubleday, 1976).

8. Bernard d'Espagnat, "The Quantum Theory and Reality." *Scientific American* (November 1979), p. 158.

Fifteen

1. R. Buckminster Fuller, *Utopia or Oblivion* (New York: Bantam, 1969), p. 271.

2. Arthur Deikman, *Personal Freedom* (New York: Grossman, 1976), pp. 1–2.

3. Henri Bergson, *Creative Evolution* (New York: The Modern Library/Random House, 1944 [orig 1911], pp. 194–200.

4. Arthur Deikman, *Personal Freedom*, p. 23.

5. Carl Sagan, *The Dragons of Eden* (New York: Random House, 1977), p. 205.

6. Fritjof Capra, *The Turning Point* (New York: Simon and Schuster, 1982), pp. 101–102.

7. Marilyn Ferguson, *The Aquarian Conspiracy* (Los Angeles: Tarcher, 1980), pp. 282–283.

8. Ken Wilber, *Up From Eden* (New York: Anchor/Doubleday, 1981), p. 9.

9. Lewis Thomas, "The Strangeness of Nature." *Human Nature* (October 1978), pp. 60–61.

FURTHER READING

An annotated bibliography of works which are not featured in the text of the book, but which amplify its theme and provide viable alternatives in evolutionary thinking.

Adams, George, and Whicher, Olive, *The Plant Between Sun and Earth* (London: Rudolph Steiner Press, 1980).
> An engrossing book, which discusses the ideas of Goethe and meta-morphosis in plants and flowers. Introduces projective geometry as a mathematical framework for the understanding of transformations in plant growth.

Adler, Robert (ed.), *Psychoneuroimmunology* (New York: Academic Press, 1981).
> Contains a great deal of research data suggestive of a relationship between emotions, stress, and immunity. While a Lamarckian evolutionary view is not specifically addressed, much of the data herein is indirect support for it, in terms of emphasizing a psyche-to-soma or psychoneurological connection.

Barthèlemy-Madaule, Madeline, *Lamarck: The Mythical Precursor* (Cambridge, Mass.: MIT Press, 1982).
> A beautifully written historical study of Lamarck. Includes a thorough bibliography of Lamarck's prolific works, as well as a lengthy compilation of works about Lamarck by international authors.

Barzun, Jacques, *Darwin, Marx, Wagner* (Garden City, N.Y.: Anchor/Doubleday, 1958).
> A classic historical treatment, graphically exposing the destructive side of mechanical materialism which, among other things, in the author's view, has been "the source of the twentieth century's characteristic problems." Illuminates Darwin's predecessors in originating the evolutionary view, such as Lamarck's mentor, Georges L. L. Buffon, and Darwin's own father (also a Lamarckian), Erasmus Darwin.

Bateson, Gregory, *Mind and Nature* (New York: Dutton, 1979).
> The late anthropologist, son of British biologist William Bateson, writes about biological evolution as a "mental" process, adding a plethora of interesting insights.

Bethell, Tom, "Darwin's Mistake." *Harper's Magazine* (February 1976).
A readable critique of Darwinian theory, with ample discussion of the tautological character.

Bertalanffy, Ludwig Von, *Robots, Men and Minds* (New York: Braziller, 1967).
Contains some excellent insights into inadequacies of Darwinism and Behaviorism. Bertalanffy, developer of General Systems Theory, also reveals why a more holistic approach is more meaningful than reductionism.

Bowler, Peter J., *The Eclipse of Darwinism* (Baltimore: Johns Hopkins University Press, 1983).
A historical and philosophical analysis of anti-Darwinian theories in the decades around 1900. While it does not take a stand either for or against Darwinism, this book provides one of the most comprehensive, in-depth treatments of alternatives in evolutionary thinking, including ample coverage of Lamarckism and neo-Lamarckism, orthogenesis, theistic evolutionary positions, and more. The role of modern creationism is also insightfully amplified upon.

Bowser, Hal, "Micro Masterpieces." *Science Digest* (December 1981).
A beautifully illustrated article about the turn-of-the-century German biologist Ernst Haeckel. Haeckel's *The Riddle of the Universe* is a *tour de force* in evolutionary, cosmic insight.

Brent, Peter, *Charles Darwin: A Man of Enlarged Curiosity* (New York: Harper and Row, 1981).
A well-written biography of Darwin, containing new, unpublished material from his letters, diaries, and autobiography. An objective report that allows the reader insight into Darwin's personality and psychological development, and an intimate account of the creative process.

Briggs, John P., and Peat, F. David, *Looking Glass Universe* (New York: Cornerstone/Simon and Schuster, 1984).
Progressive scientific thinking at its best, with fresh observations/discussion on evolution and the ideas of Prigogine, Jantsch, and Sheldrake. An effort is made to integrate various scientific disciplines and to move toward a new and "emerging world-view."

Burkhardt, Richard W., Jr., *The Spirit of System* (Cambridge, Mass.: Harvard University Press, 1977).
A classic treatment of the evolutionary biology of Jean Baptiste Lamarck.

Cole, G. D. H., *Samuel Butler* (London: Longmans, Green and Co., 1952).
A comprehensive, yet concise review of Butler's life and works, with a valuable bibliography of Butler's abundant and diverse writings.

Corning, Peter A., *The Synergism Hypothesis* (New York: McGraw-Hill, 1983).
Subtitled "A Theory of Progressive Evolution," this is essentially another modern synthesis (i.e., an apologia) of Darwinism. It is a highly academic treatment, with innumerable footnotes and notes, technical terminology, and the like. By recognizing synergy or "interactionism," the implication is that an important new principle is being brought into evolutional conceptualization. Yet, without mentioning Mr. Synergy himself, Buck-

minster Fuller, or his work, Corning uses the principle to account for everything from teleonomy to politics. Attempting such a "grand sweep" with nothing but selection and synergy amounts to little more than a grand unlikelihood.

Cronin, Vincent, *The View from Planet Earth* (New York: Morrow, 1981).
A re-creation of the cosmology of each historical age through its key figures. Noteworthy is the final chapter of the book, titled "Chance or Design," wherein Cronin reveals the pitfalls in the randomness explanation of cosmogenesis and evolution.

Cudmore, L. L. Larison, *The Center of Life* (New York: Quadrangles, 1977).
While operating from a selectionist position, Cudmore is still able to provide a fascinating view of contemporary biology, with some interesting and original sidelights.

Degrood, David H., *Haeckel's Theory of the Unity of Nature* (Boston: Christopher, 1965).
A clear account of Ernst Haeckel's philosophy of universal evolution. Like Spencer and Butler, Haeckel recognized the importance of a comprehensive (nonreductionistic) approach to the question of evolution.

Deikman, Arthur J., *The Observing Self* (Boston: Beacon Press, 1982).
Explores links between contemporary science and ancient systems of wisdom, including some valuable insights into the notion of "conscious evolution."

Ditfurth, Hoimar V., *The Origins of Life* (San Francisco: Harper and Row, 1983).
Subtitled "Evolution as Creation," this work provides a lucid, in-depth reconciliation of the apparent contradictions in creationism and scientism. Unlike most scientists, Ditfurth reflects in his writings the position that evolution "constitutes a principle that stretches far beyond the realm of biology ... an event that encompasses the entire universe."

DuNoüy, Lecomte, *Human Destiny* (New York: Mentor, 1947).
An internationally popular bestseller, it contains one of the best expositions available on spiritual man and human evolution, from a non-Darwinian perspective.

Duncan, Ronald, and Weston-Smith, Miranda (eds.), *The Encyclopedia of Ignorance* (Oxford: Pergamon Press, 1976).
A collection of original articles on the state of contemporary scientific "ignorance," it contains a couple of good critiques (one by John Maynard Smith and the other by E. W. F. Tomlin) of the "modern synthesis."

Durant, Will, *The Story of Philosophy* (New York: Washington Square Press Pocket Books, 1953).
Provides comprehensive, yet clear and understandable coverage on many of the world's greatest philosophers, from Plato to Dewey. His treatments of Spencer and Bergman are superb, and especially their views on evolution.

Edberg, Rolf, *The Dream of Kilimanjaro* (New York: Pantheon, 1976).
A beautifully written book which contains excellent insights on evolution with a minimum of Darwinism.

Elliot, Hugh, *Herbert Spencer* (New York: Holt and Co., 1917).
An excellent book, on the life and works of Herbert Spencer. Spencer's evolutionary system is well covered and clarified.

Fine, Paul E. M., "Lamarckian Ironies in Contemporary Biology." *Lancet* (June 2, 1979).
A remarkably parsimonious, yet well-written article in which a great deal of recent evidence is reviewed which signals the need for a shift to a neo-Lamarckian perspective.

Fix, William R., *The Bone Peddlers* (New York: Macmillan, 1984).
Easily one of the finest books available on the entire subject of evolution. Fix provides an objective treatment, encompassing "a dazzling challenge to the smug conceits of evolutionary scientists, as well as to the emotional machinations of creationists."

Foy, Sally, and Oxford Scientific Films, *The Grand Design* (Englewood Cliffs, N.J.: Prentice-Hall, 1983).
Containing over 300 color photographs, this book graphically illuminates geometry, form, and function in nature.

Gliedman, John, "Beyond the Brain's Boundaries." *Science Digest* (February 1983).
A well-written article about Rupert Sheldrake and his ideas, with some useful, thought-provoking discussion.

Gould, Stephen J. *The Panda's Thumb* (New York: W. W. Norton, 1980).
An examination of evolution which follows up on Gould's *Ever Since Darwin*.

Grassé, Pierre P., *Evolution of Living Organisms* (New York: Academic Press, 1978).
Grassé, a biologist, is one of the few academic writers who is able to depart from Darwinian dogma in a way which can be considered scientific.

Greenough, William T., *The Nature and Nurture of Behavior: Developmental Psychobiology* (Readings from *Scientific American*). (San Francisco: W. H. Freeman, 1973).
Contains at least four research articles which establish that environmental and/or sociopsychological deprivation in infancy and childhood can lead to structural as well as behavioral change in the adolescent and adult. Two of these articles which make this very clear are: "Deprivation Dwarfism" by Lytl I. Gardner, and "Brain Changes in Response to Experience" by Mark R. Rosenzweig, et al. Both articles suggest that the structural changes that result from environmental or experiential deprivation are mediated by hormonal (and hence genetic) alteration.

Grene, Marjorie, *The Knower and the Known* (London: Faber, 1969).
This outstanding book by an eminent philosopher contains a chapter titled "The Faith of Darwinism" as well as an appended essay, "Statistics and Selection: An Analysis of Fischer's Genetical Theory," which presents a thorough and effective critique of neo-Darwinism.

Hitching, Francis, "Was Darwin Wrong?" *Life* (April 1982).
A fine critique of neo-Darwinism (as well as creationism) that attempts to generate alternative explanations for evolution. The article is an excerpt from Hitching's recent book *The Neck of the Giraffe: Where Darwin Went Wrong* (London: Ticknor and Fields, 1982).

Hoyle, Fred, *Evolution from Space* (Hillside, N.J.: Enslow Publishers, 1982).
Contains Hoyle's superb arguments discrediting the randomness concept in (Darwinian) accounts of evolution. His alternative to Darwinism, that terrestrial evolution got its start from micro-organisms originating in outer space, might be considered just as ludicrous. A similar argument was put forth recently by Francis Crick (of Watson and Crick fame), however far more speculative, implying that extraterrestrial civilizations deliberately seeded our planet with life.

Huntley, H. E., *The Divine Proportion* (New York: Dover, 1970).
An exceptional book, it elaborates on the theme of "a natural aesthetic which corresponds to a universal order." Contains some excellent analyses of the phenomenon of beauty and design in nature.

Iqbal, Afzal, *The Life and Work of Jalalludin Rumi* (London: Octagon, 1984).
Written for the general public, this book outlines the life and ideas of one of the greatest sages who ever lived. Includes valuable coverage on Rumi's conceptions on creative evolution, which preceded Bergson (and Darwin) by six centuries.

Jaffe, Aniela, *The Myth of Meaning* (New York: G. P. Putnam's Sons, 1971).
An intimate associate of the late C. G. Jung, Jaffe presents clear and intelligent insights into Jung's concepts (collective unconscious, archetypes, instincts) of evolutionary relevance.

Jaki, Stanley L., *The Road of Science and the Ways to God* (Chicago: University of Chicago Press, 1978).
Originally presented as the Gifford Lectures for 1975 and 1976 at the University of Edinburgh, this work endeavors to bridge the gap between science and theology. The chapter titled "Pointers of Purpose" is one of the best available philosophical analyses of the shortfall inherent in Darwinism, and also makes a case for the notions of design and purpose in evolution.

Joad, C. E. M., *Guide to Philosophy* (New York: Dover, 1967).
An in-depth critical treatment of several key issues, including "scientific materialism," which encompasses behaviorism and Darwinism. The inadequacies in materialism/mechanistics are clearly delineated. Also contains a chapter on the psychological and evolutionary ideas of Henri Bergson.

Jones, F. Wood, *Habit and Heritage* (London: Kegan Paul, 1943).
A rarely cited work, which ranks along with Cecil P. Martin's *Psychology, Evolution, and Sex* as not only scientifically exact in exposing the shortcomings of neo-Darwinism but in its assemblage of empirical evidence to substantiate a transformist position. This work by Jones complements his earlier work, *The Matrix of Mind* (London: Kegan Paul, 1929).

King, Ursula, *Towards a New Mysticism* (New York: Seabury, 1981).
About human and spiritual evolution, this is the definitive work on the ideas of Teilhard de Chardin.

Koestler, Arthur, *Bricks to Babel* (New York: Random House, 1980).
A choice selection of 50 years of Koestler's writings, with fresh commentary supplied by the author. Contains many pieces on Koestler's brand of neo-Lamarckism and his theory of the holarchy.

Koestler, Arthur, "Nothing But ...?" in R. Duncan and M. Weston-Smith (eds.), *Lying Truths* (Oxford: Pergamon Press, 1979).
A parsimonious essay in which Koestler expresses his views on the precarious, reductionistic foundations of modern biological and behavioral science.

Krutch, Joseph Wood, *The Great Chain of Life* (Boston: Houghton Mifflin, 1977).
Contains numerous illuminations of non-Darwinian evolution by one of the greatest naturalists of all time.

Land, George T. L., *Grow or Die: The Unifying Principle of Transformation* (New York: Delta/Dell, 1973).
Possibly the finest contemporary, scientific exposition on the phenomenon of transformation in nature and life. Ties in a broad spectrum of data and subject matter, yet remains comprehensive and comprehensible.

Laudan, Larry, *Progress and Its Problems* (Berkeley: University of California Press, 1977).
A comprehensive analysis of paradigms, world views, and related phenomena of socio-scientific interest.

Lovelock, J. E., *Gaia* (New York: Oxford University Press, 1979).
Gaia (after the Greek Earth Goddess) is synonymous with earth (and its oceans and atmosphere) as a self-regulatory organism. This insightful idea has of course baffled Darwinists, causing them to ask such staggering questions as "How does a species of one evolve? There's nothing for natural selection to select among" (Doolittle, W. Ford, "Is Nature Really Motherly?" *CoEvolution Quarterly*, Spring 1981). With a change of reference Gaia makes a great deal of sense, and in fact is antedated by Gustav Fechner's *A Pluralistic Universe* (London: Longmans, Green and Co., 1909)—a masterpiece in innovative evolutionary thinking.

MacBeth, Norman, *Darwin Retried* (New York: Delta/Dell, 1971).
A definitive critique of neo-Darwinism based upon "rules of evidence" by an unrelenting attorney.

Mackenzie, Deborah, "The Electricity That Shapes Our Ends." *New Scientist* (January 28, 1982).
> A readable review of evidence which suggests that bioelectricity is a key factor in fertilization, embryogenesis, and morphogenesis. While the research cited certainly lends support to Rupert Sheldrake's ideas, Sheldrake is unfortunately not mentioned.

Martin, C. P., "A Non-Geneticist Looks at Evolution." *American Scientist* (January 1953).
> For obvious reasons a rarely cited article that is nonetheless one of the best available exposing weaknesses in neo-Darwinian theory from a scientific perspective. As in his book *Psychology, Evolution and Sex*, Martin amasses evidence for his neo-Lamarckian alternative, "lingering modifications."

McWaters, Barry, *Conscious Evolution* (Los Angeles: New Age Press, 1981).
> A readable and unconventional book, of interest to anyone disenchanted with dry, technical treatments of evolutional subject matter.

Morris, Richard, *Evolution and Human Nature* (New York: Seaview/Putnam, 1983).
> Clearly written, this book examines the problem of human nature in light of evolution. Morris's critique of sociobiology is insightful, as is his understanding of the cultural and political forces that help shape and maintain certain kinds of evolutionary views.

Nisbet, Robert, *Prejudices* (Cambridge, Mass.: Harvard University Press, 1982).
> While containing an abundance of food for thought, Nisbet's critiques of Darwinism, sociobiology, and creationism are unparalleled in their depth and penetrability.

Ornstein, Robert, *The Mind Field* (New York: Pocket Books/Simon and Schuster, 1978).
> A collection of insightful essays by an original thinker and scientist. Contains much information on the difference between bogus and authentic Eastern systems of development as well as chapters on evolution and the brain.

Ouspensky, P. D., *The Psychology of Man's Possible Evolution* (New York: Vintage/Random House, 1973).
> An introduction to the notion of "deliberate evolution," as conceptualized in the teachings of the Russian master G. I. Gurdjieff.

Polanyi, Michael, *Personal Knowledge* (Chicago: University of Chicago Press, 1958).
> While expertly covering a wide range of subject matter, the final chapters of this book raise several points of contention vis-à-vis Darwinism and other forms of conventional biological thinking.

Progoff, Ira, *Depth Psychology* (New York: Julian Press, 1969).
> A superb book which draws certain key parallels between depth (mind) psychology and alternative conceptions of evolution, like those of Jan Christian Smuts and Edmund Sinnot. His section titled "Man's Capacity

for Self-Transformation" is extremely valuable, and in some sense (since this was written in the sixties) ahead of its time.

Rafi-ud-din, M., *Ideology of the Future* (Lahore, Pakistan: Ashraf, 1946).
Alongside Lecomte DuNoüy's *Human Destiny*, no better book has been written that effectively blends spirituality and evolution. The scope of this book is immense, including chapters on politics, education, history, and art, encompassed within Rafi-ud-din's Bergsonian evolutionary framework. As remarkable a book as this one is, even more remarkable is the fact that it is virtually unknown in the West.

Randall, John L., *Parapsychology and the Nature of Life* (New York: Harper and Row, 1975).
In the introduction, Duke University's J. B. Rhine offers that "Randall ventures to speak out on the larger meaning he sees in the findings of psi research for the nature of life itself." Contains a good analysis of evolution from a fresh point of view.

Rifkin, Jeremy, *Algeny* (New York: Viking Press, 1983).
While essentially an admonition to society to be cautious in its somewhat overanxious attempts to develop biotechnology, this book contains an excellent critique of Darwinism, as well as many original and progressive viewpoints. If anything, this book is an effective thought provoker.

Rose, Steven (ed.), *Towards a Liberatory Biology* (London: Allison and Busby, 1982).
A collection of original articles, many critical of biological reductionism. Several of the articles also point out inadequacies in neo-Darwinism from a scientific standpoint. An article by Mae-Wan Ho and Peter T. Saunders ("Adaptation and Natural Selection: Mechanism and Teleology") intimates possible mechanisms underlying the Lamarckian principle of the inheritance of acquired characteristics.

Russell, Peter, *The Global Brain* (Los Angeles: J. P. Tarcher, 1983).
Some fascinating speculations "on the evolutionary leap to planetary consciousness." A true study in lateral, right-brain thinking.

Salk, Jonas, *Anatomy of Reality* (New York: Columbia University Press, 1983).
An enlightening discussion of evolution (primarily human evolution) in a new perspective. Salk's notion of "metabiological evolution" is akin to a culturally based evolution, with Lamarckian overtones; however, Salk is still committed to a Darwinian interpretation regarding what he calls "biological evolution." This is still an invaluable contribution to our understanding of psychology and the dilemma of modern existence.

An insightful interview with Dr. Salk, also on the topic of evolution, is contained in *Psychology Today* (March 1983), pp. 50–56.

Samples, Bob, *Mind of Our Mother* (New York: Addison-Wesley, 1981).
Subtitled "Toward Holonomy and Planetary Consciousness," this is an entertaining yet well-written book about evolution and consciousness in nature.

Sanai, Hakim, "The Abode of Spring" (trans. by David Pendlebury), in *Four Sufi Classics* (Introduction by Idries Shah) (London: Octagon Press, 1980).
> Written about 1111 A.D. by the renowned Sufi sage Sanai of Ghazna. Although encompassing a broad range, this work spans evolution from a personal perspective, with intimations as to the "purpose and meaning of life."

Schumaker, E. F., *A Guide for the Perplexed* (New York: Harper and Row, 1975).
> A collection of essays by the late author of *Small Is Beautiful*. The chapter titled "Science and Evolution" reveals the anti-Darwinian bent of this probing thinker.

Schoffeniels, Ernest, *Anti-Chance* (Oxford: Pergamon Press, 1976).
> Written as a rebuttal to Jacques Monod's *Chance and Necessity* (a tome of pure, positivisitic neo-Darwinism), this is also an excellent scientific (albeit technical) treatise in support of neo-Lamarckism, drawing upon much contemporary research in biogenetics and biochemistry (Dr. Schoffeniels is a Professor of Biochemistry, University of Liège, France).

Scott, Ernest, *The People of the Secret* (London: Octagon, 1983).
> Explores the possibility that both biological evolution and human history are under the influence of a "hierarchy of Intelligences," of which "the lowest level...makes physical contact with mankind."

Shah, Idries, *Learning How to Learn* (New York: Harper and Row, 1981).
> Insights and information on such diverse topics as society, spirituality, psychology, learning, and higher evolution. A companion to this work is *A Perfumed Scorpion* (New York: Harper and Row, 1982).

Sinnott, Edmund W., *The Biology of Spirit* (Los Angeles: Science of Mind Publications, 1973).
> Originally written in 1953, this classic clearly elucidates the shortfall inherent in the contemporary, reductionistic approach to biology, and makes a case for an expanded view, encompassing purpose, motive, design, and spirit.

Smith, Huston, *Forgotten Truth* (New York: Harper and Row, 1976).
> A comprehensive treatment of science and spirituality, including a full chapter which expertly challenges the premises of neo-Darwinism.

Smith, Maynard (ed.), *Evolution Now* (San Francisco: W. H. Freeman, 1982).
> A good review of modern thinking on evolution, with some leeway allowed for a Lamarckian position, at least as it pertains to findings in immunology.

Smuts, Jan, *Holism and Evolution* (New York: Macmillan, 1926).
> The originator of the term "holism," which is now almost a cliche. An insightful book, which was far ahead of its time, but which may soon experience a revival of interest.

Steele, E. J., *Somatic Selection and Adaptive Evolution* (Chicago: University of Chicago Press, 1981).

The most complete and convincing exposition on the scientific basis of neo-Lamarckism.

Stevens, Anthony, *Archetypes* (New York: Morrow, 1982).
Illuminates the biological basis of Jungian theory. While acknowledging that Jung's concepts of archetype and the collective unconscious call for a Lamarckian interpretation, a Darwinian bias disallows further elaboration. Nonetheless, this superb book can be taken as one of the most conclusive arguments in favor of evolutionary transformism and the role played by racial memory in the human evolutionary process.

Stevens, Peter S., *Patterns in Nature* (Boston: Little, Brown and Co., 1974).
A beautifully illustrated and photographically replete exposition which "explores the universal patterns in which nature expresses herself." A superlative synthesis of art and science.

Taylor, Gordon Rattray, *The Great Evolution Mystery* (New York: Harper and Row, 1983).
Taylor's last work before his death in 1981, this is, like Hitching's *The Neck of the Giraffe*, one of the best critiques of modern Darwinism, including an unprejudiced, erudite treatment of neo-Lamarckism.

Thorpe, W. H., *Purpose in a World of Chance* (Oxford: Oxford University Press, 1978).
Described as a "biologist's view of life and evolution, mind, the self, and the idea of deity," this book presents scientifically based arguments (and evidence) to suggest that randomness is a feeble biological concept vis-à-vis purpose, order, and design.

Tompkins, Peter, and Bird, Christopher, *The Secret Life of Plants* (New York: Avon, 1973).
Eye-opening coverage of the inner world of plants and the intuitive insights of leading plant specialists, such as India's Sir Jagadis Chandra Bose, Goethe, Fechner, Luther Burbank, and George Washington Carver; subtitled "A Fascinating Account of the Physical, Emotional, and Spiritual Relations Between Plants and Men."

Tufail, Ibin (trans. by Riad Kocache), *The Journey of the Soul* (London: Octagon, 1982).
Written in the 12th century, its ideas on empiricism and evolution predate Darwin by seven hundred years. Considered one of the most enlightened pieces of literature of the Middle Ages, it is widely regarded as the prototype for Daniel Defoe's *Robinson Crusoe*.

Von Frisch, Karl, *Animal Architecture* (New York: Harcourt, Brace, Jovanovich, 1974).
Von Frisch, a Nobel Laureate, is best known for his studies of bees, and true to form, again provides us with a thorough and revealing view of the purposefulness and brilliance of the behavior of our animal cousins.

Waliullah, Shah (trans. by J. N. Jalbani), *Sufism and the Islamic Tradition* (London: Octagon, 1980).

Among many other things, here is an 18th-century statement on evolution, with Platonic and spiritual implications.

Walker, Kenneth, *Life's Long Journey* (New York: Thomas Nelson, 1961).
An excellent non-Darwinian account of evolution, emphasizing the views of Bergson and Butler.

Wiens, John A., "Competition or Peaceful Coexistence." *Natural History* (March 1983).
Wiens, a University of New Mexico professor of biology, makes a good case for his position that "in some environments, the 'great battle of life' involves less competition than Darwinian theorists once assumed."

Wilber, Ken (ed.), *The Holographic Paradigm* (Boulder: Shambhala, 1982).
Speculation on the hologramic brain, with some very original discussion on the relationship between brain, behavior, and evolution.

Williams, Cora Lenore, *Creative Involution* (New York: Knopf, 1916).
Meant as a companion volume to Bergson's *Creative Evolution*, Williams' work presents an excellent treatment on involution—the psychospiritual unfolding process considered the inner counterpart to external, visible evolution.

Williams, Leonard, *Challenge to Survival* (New York: Harper and Row, 1977).
Subtitled "A Philosophy of Evolution." Anthropologist Williams presents rare insights, including salient points vis-à-vis neo-Darwinian shortcomings.

Wilson, Colin, *The Occult* (New York: Vintage/Random House, 1973).
A fine treatment of the paranormal, with a chapter on human evolution from a non-Darwinian perspective.

Wolkomir, Richard, "The Wizard of Ooze," *Omni* (January 1985).
An interesting article about Lynn Margulis's theory of symbiotic evolution. Because her theory challenges certain key premises in neo-Darwinism, the article exposes how Margulis has met with serious resistance from within the scientific community itself.

INDEX

accidental mutation. *See* random mutation
Act of Creation, The (Koestler), 12
adenosine monophosphate (AMP), cyclical, 120–22
Agar, W. E., 136–37
aggression, 32–33
altruism, 43
a posteriori inference, 53
Aquarian Conspiracy, The (Ferguson), 175

Barash, David P., 41
Barfield, Owen, 72
Barfield, R. H., 18
Baskin, Yvonne, 195
Bentov, Itzhak, 23–24, 77–78
Bergson, Henri, 98–99, 130, 140, 170–71
Bertalanffy, Ludwig von, 49, 63, 66, 77, 81
Beyond Good and Evil (Nietzsche), 101
Bible
    allegorical interpretation of, 7–8, 30
    as temporary construction, 8
Big Bang theory, 23–24
biogenetic research, 105, 126–27
    on brain, 107
    cyclic AMP, 120–22
    on hormonal regulation, 112–14
    on memory, 115–20
    non-Mendelian genes in, 108–9
    on reproductive system, 123–26
    on Watson-Crick dogma, 109–12
brain
    anatomy of, 145–46
    compensatory potential of, 148
    and gene mutation, 107
    global mind-brain, 152–53
    hologram analogy, 79, 148–49
    hypothalamus-pituitary feedback, 114, 115
    mental set of, 147–48
    and reproductive system, 123–26
    right/left specialization, 31, 76–77,
        146–47, 170, 171, 176
    role in evolution, 169–70
    second messengers to, 120–22
    size, 30, 144, 152
Brilliant, Ashleigh, 50
Bucke, Maurice, 18
Burr, Harold Saxton, 130, 132, 141, 160
Butler, Samuel, 91, 92–95, 97, 158

Campbell, Edward, 135
cancer, psychological factors in, 133
Cannon, H. Graham, 91, 101
Capra, Fritjof, 97, 174–75
cell division, 26–27, 132

central nervous system (CNS), 107, 132, 145,
    152, 157–58, 169
    See also brain
cerebral cortex, 145, 146, 169
chlorophyll, 26
Clausen, Jens, 65
coevolution, 69–70
Commoner, Barry, 109
competition, Darwinian, 64-66, 70
Complete Man, 167, 173, 177, 178
computer memory, 194–95
consciousness
    animal, 154, 156
    ascending levels of, 153–54, 177–78, 183
    bimodal, 170-72
    crisis, 167–68, 172, 175
    global, 190, 191
    and learning, 96
    and morphology, 182–83
    planetary, 152
    and science, 176
cosmos, dynamic, 45–46
creationism, 6–7, 8, 104, 158–59
Creation of Life, The (Smith), 187–88
creative evolution, 98–99, 170–71
Creative Evolution (Bergson), 98
Creator, 178, 199–200
Crew, A. E., 136–37
Crews, David, 123, 126
Crow, James F., 108
cyclical AMP (adenosine monophosphate), 120–22

Darwin, Charles, 36, 37–39, 145, 186, 188
Darwinism
    classical, 37–39, 50–51
    debate with Lamarckians, 97–98
    evidence for, 36–37
        contradictory, 60–72
    limitations of, 72–73
    logical fallacies of, 50–52
    Marx on, 186–87
    mathematical improbabilities of, 54–59
    mechanistic reductionism of, 48–50
    neo-Darwinism, 39–41, 178–79
    and paradigm shift, 12–13
    reasons for acceptance, 48
    social, 48, 186
    synthetic theory of, 41–42, 44, 71
    tautological errors of, 52–54
    ultra-Darwinism, 43–46
    Wallace and, 188–89
    as world view, 8
    and *Zeitgeist* change, 14–16, 189–91

Grateful acknowledgment is made to the following publishers for permission to reprint portions of these materials:

John, E. Roy, "Derepressor Hypotheses," *Mechanisms of Memory*, New York; Academic Press, 1967 · Skolimowski, Henryk, "Evolutionary Illuminations." *Alternate Futures*, Fall, 1980 · Hammarskjold, Dag, *Markings*, New York: Ballantine Books, 1983 · Darwin, Francis, *The Life and Letters of Charles Darwin*, New York: Basic Books, 1959 · Waters, Frank, as quoted in Smith, Robert W., "Standing Tall" in *The Bloomsbury Review*, September, 1984 · Lindegren, Carl, and Margulis, Lynn, "Dogma and Iconoclasm in Biology: The Gene Is Not Enough," *Co-Evolution Quarterly*, Summer, 1980 · Thomas, Lewis, "On the Nature of Cooperation," *Discover*, November, 1981 · Restak, Richard, *The Brain: The Last Frontier*, New York: Doubleday, 1979 · Cannon, H. Graham, *Lamark and Modern Genetics*, Westport, CT: Greenwood Press, 1959 · Deikman, Arthur, *Personal Freedom*, New York: Grossman/Viking, 1976 · Schumacher, E.F., *A Guide For The Perplexed*, New York: Harper & Row, 1977; Roszak, Theodore, *Unfinished Animal*, New York: Harper & Row, 1975 · Goethe, Johann Wolfgang (quote), Vietor, Karl, *Goethe*, Cambridge: Harvard University Press, 1950; Wordsworth, William, "The Daisy," *Wordsworth: Poetry and Prose*, Harvard University Press, 1967 · Kleefeld, Carolyn, *Climates of the Mind*, Big Sur: The Horse & Bird Press, 1979 · Krutch, Joseph Wood, *The Great Chain of Life*, Boston: Houghton Mifflin Company, 1956; Murchie, Guy, *The Seven Mysteries of Life*, Houghton Mifflin Company, 1978 · Fuller, Buckminster (with Applewhite, E.J.), *Synergetics*, New York: Macmillan, 1975 · Underhill, Evelyn, *Mysticism*, New York: Meridian/New American Library, 1955 · Bergson, Henri, *Creative Evolution*, New York: The Modern Library/Random House, 1944 · Wiens, John A., "Competition or Peaceful Coexistence?" *Natural History*, March, 1983 · Rumi, Jalalludin, *The Masnavi: Teachings of Rumi*, London: Octagon Press, 1973; Scott, Ernest, *The People of the Secret*, Octagon Press, 1983 · Jantsch, Eric, *The Self-Organizing Universe*, New York: Pergamon Press, 1980 · Fuller, R. Buckminster, *Operating Manual for Spaceship Earth*, New York: Pocket Books, 1970 · Sagan, Carl, *The Dragons of Eden*, New York: Random House, 1977 · Fiddes, John C., "The Nucleotide Sequence of Viral DNA," *Scientific American*, December, 1977 · Capra, Fritjof, *The Tao of Physics*, Boulder: Shambhala Publications, Inc., 1975 · Capra, Fritjof, *The Turning Point*, New York: Simon & Schuster, 1982; Watson, Lyall, *Lifetide*, Simon & Schuster and John Brockman, 1981 · Shaw, George Bernard, *Man and Superman*, Society of Authors on behalf of the Bernard Shaw Estate · Pauwels, Louis, and Berger, Jacques, *The Morning of the Magicians*, New York: Stein and Day,

1964 · Ferguson, Marilyn, *The Aquarian Conspiracy*, J.P. Tarcher, Inc., Houghton Mifflin Company, and Granada Publishing Ltd., 1980 · Nietzsche, Friedrich, *Beyond Good and Evil*, New York: Vintage/Random House, 1966; Ouspensky, P.D., *A New Model of the Universe*, Vintage/Random House, 1971; Rose, Steven, *The Conscious Brain*, Vintage/Random House, 1976 · Dobzhansky, Theodosius, Ayala, Francisco J., Stebbing G. Ledyars, and Valentino, James W., *Evolution*, New York: W.H. Freeman, 1977; Segal, Sheldon J., "The Physiology of Human Reproduction," *Scientific American*, 1974, reprinted in Rae Silver and Harvey H. Feder (eds.) *Hormones and Reproductive Behavior: Readings from Scientific American*, San Francisco: W.H. Freeman, 1979 · Brilliant, Ashleigh, *I May Not Be Totally Perfect, but Parts of Me Are Excellent*, Santa Barbara: Woodbridge, 1979.